Date Due

1/13/70		
3/11/70		
DEC 27 1973		
FEB 15 1978		
OCT 10 1978		
JE 30 '86		
NO 16 88		
Dec 6 88		
Jan 3 88		
JE 16 '89		
OCT 16 96		
MAY 02 97		
JUN 30 97		
OC 11 7		

W9-AKD-933

PROUD WARRIOR:
The Story of Black Hawk

PROUD WARRIOR:
The Story of Black Hawk

by Marion Lawson

Illustrated by W. T. Mars

Hawthorn Books, Inc.

Publishers   New York

2435

For Phil

Acknowledgments

PROUD WARRIOR: The Story of Black Hawk is based on Black Hawk's autobiography dictated to Antoine LeClaire for translation and first published in 1833. Some of Black Hawk's own words are used in the telling. Speeches of Black Hawk, Keokuk and others, with slight changes and omissions, are quoted as recorded at the time.

Documents and later histories of the period, a study of Indian customs in libraries and museums, and visits to the area of the story also contributed much information.

The author is particularly grateful to Dr. Frederick J. Dockstader, Director of the Museum of the American Indian, Heye Foundation, New York City for granting the use of the Museum's library and for answering many questions.

M. L.

Contents

1. Return to Saukenuk

Paddles flashed over the flood-high waters. Horses, led or ridden by the strong young hunters and warriors, were trotting down the forest trails. Spring, Mannocumink, was calling the Sauk people home to Saukenuk from the winter hunting grounds.

Dugouts, elm bark canoes, a few of birch bark—much mended and greatly treasured by the Old Ones—swept in a long procession down the Mashisepu, the Great River.

In one of the first canoes sat Black Hawk with his father Pyesa. His mother, Ketikwe, followed close behind, her canoe laden with household pots, carrying baskets, the family's share of the spring's sugar making, and the cattail mats they used to build their winter lodges.

Black Hawk, a boy of thirteen, straight-backed and slight of build, stared eagerly ahead. His quick, dark hazel eyes recognized every familiar landmark as their peltry-laden canoes moved past bluffs and prairies.

Rocky Island (Rock Island, Illinois) was before them, a great solid rock splitting the river, crowned with fertile soil and richly wooded. Following the main channel they moved close to the Island, past the caves where the Good Spirit lived.

For Black Hawk the remembered sweetness of honeysuckle filled the air. His eyes danced as he thought of the wild grapes, gooseberries, plums, and all the berries the boys would enjoy again this summer—if they got to the Island before the women began the fruit drying.

He sent a mischievous glance back at Ketikwe. His father grunted and Black Hawk resumed his paddling.

That winter's hunt had been a good one. Traders had collected many furs at their winter camp, but they were bringing home a choice lot of beaver, mink, otter, muskrat, bear, raccoon and deer. Some would be kept by the women for their own family's use, the rest would be sold to the traders who came to Saukenuk.

In March the Sauks had left their winter camp on the Skunk River and their hunting grounds in the Iowa River country. They moved north to make sugar camp in the country west of the Great River, on Yellow Creek, above Prairie du Chien. When the late winter hunting parties had joined them, they feasted on maple sugar and the plentiful wild fowl before starting home.

They did not stop at Rocky Island. They wanted no delay, nor did Black Hawk, for he knew the wild fruits were not yet even in blossom.

The procession swept onward. Voices rose higher, like the humming of bees when they swarmed, thought Black Hawk. His father grunted. Black Hawk bent to his paddle as the lead canoes changed course, left the Mississippi, and rounding the point through turbulent waters, started up the Rock River.

"Almost there," said Black Hawk, imitating the dignified composure of his father.

"Very soon now," said Pyesa.

Three miles up river where willows lined the bank, the canoes began drawing shoreward. Black Hawk dropped his paddle, gathered up his small bundle of treasures and his bow and arrow, carefully wrapped in its deerskin case. He leaped into the shallows and splashed through the water, unmindful of soaking his moccasins.

With the return of the tribe to Senisepo Kebesaukee, a point of land lying between the Rock and Mississippi Rivers, the Indian village that had drowsed unoccupied through the winter moons sprang into bustling life.

Fox Squirrel and other boys followed Black Hawk up the trail. Whooping, they raced through the village and entered the central square.

Black Hawk bounded off to be the first of his family to reach their lodge. Pyesa and Ketikwe, his aunts and uncles and the smaller children would soon be swarming along with household goods, dried meats, furs, and maple sugar, all the products of their winter's work and hunting.

Black Hawk threw his blanket aside and stood before the lodge in deerskin breechclout and moccasins, surveying his home with cocked head.

It had withstood winter storms with little damage. In places a few of the elm bark slabs had worked loose. Some animal had knocked away one of the supporting posts of the shed over the east doorway. But his mother would soon have that fixed and when she got the squash vines growing on the fence all would be as it had been every summer.

He looked approvingly at the village with its rows of lodges —nearly a hundred of them—stretching out from the central square. It was a much cleaner, more orderly looking village than that of their careless relatives in the Fox village up the Mississippi.

"The mats, my little Sparrow Hawk," his mother was calling, "Help bring up the mats."

Black Hawk frowned at her use of his nickname, Sparrow. Perhaps he was a bit thinner than the other boys, but he would fill out. Before many summers he would be as strong and powerful as the hawk after which he had been named, Mukute Mishikakak.

Now he was still young enough that he must obey her orders before he joined the other boys dawdling at the edge of the crowd around the traders. He was not yet old enough to sit with the men while, talking and smoking, they discussed their winter's exploits, bragging of the number of beavers trapped, and the scalps taken when the hunters had encountered the Osage or Sioux trespassing on their hunting grounds.

Black Hawk ran toward the river. There, pushing his way through the crowd, he took up rolls of cattail mats to be stored among the rafters of the lodge. In the lodge Pyesa hung his otter skin war bundle—that sacred bundle of charms that gave success in war—in the northwest corner of the lodge. Then, loaded down with beaver skins, he headed for the waiting traders.

Ketikwe arranged blankets and sleeping robes on the wide shelves that ran the length of the lodge on two sides. Beneath them she stored her household equipment.

The aunts, whose families occupied the other end of the big lodge, had lit small fires in the middle space. Here the women would do the cooking. When warmer weather came the fires were built outside. Black Hawk preferred this. There were more chances to help himself to some savory bit from the cooking pots. If they caught him he jumped up and down beyond their reach, laughing as they scolded.

Soon the real feasting would begin, when trading was done and those who had died during the winter were properly buried and mourned. For then the women opened the *caches* —those deep, carefully lined pits covered with sod. Here, concealed against theft, they had buried a portion of last year's crops so skilfully no stranger could find the place.

In a few days everything was in order. The Sauk people settled into the round of summer activities.

One day Black Hawk overheard the women gossiping among themselves while they worked about the lodge. A boy with blue eyes had been born during the winter, a strange thing. They were still talking of it. The baby's mother was part white, they said. She'd named him Keokuk.

Black Hawk pretended to pay no attention but he worked his mouth in disgust. Then he spat with skilled precision at a passing dog, who shook his head and snapped at him. Blue eyes. Pooh, a half-breed, one of those.

Other things were nibbling at his mind that summer, like the fleas of the dog he had insulted. All morning with other boys he had listened to the droning voices of the old men. So much must be learned from those who had lived so many moons and now might be near the singing of their death song. A boy must know the things a Sauk warrior needed to know. Of late he had grown impatient for his time of manhood to come.

Pyesa sat in the shade of his doorway, smoking and meditating. Replete from the days of feasting, he pondered the problems of a family man. Ketikwe knelt nearby. With mortar and pestle she pounded dried corn from the past winter's *cache* into meal. The kettle bubbled and steamed over the open fire.

Scowling, Black Hawk marched up to his father and stood before him, waiting until Pyesa should recognize his presence. When Pyesa's glance flickered over him and his eyebrows lifted in question, Black Hawk spoke.

"How old must I be before I can go to war?"

"When you are a man and ready."

"I am a man."

Black Hawk swelled his chest and made his muscles big, frowning as he had seen older men do.

Pyesa smiled a little, nodding agreeably.

"First, you must be a good hunter," he said. "That is the way we do in Saukenuk."

"Yes, Father. Last year when you let me try your gun and I killed the ducks—remember—you said yourself that I did well. You have seen me shoot the fish with my bow and arrow."

Pyesa was nodding in agreement.

"You yourself said I knew all the animal tracks well."

"Have patience, my son. One must learn to hunt with great skill in order to live. Warriors know that. The time will come." Pyesa was silent before he added, "You have heard the talk?"

Black Hawk's head drooped.

"Hiding with Fox Squirrel and the other boys back of the council lodge? Trying to hear of what they talked, perhaps?" said Pyesa gently, staring off toward the sky, pretending not to look at his son.

Nodding, Black Hawk admitted it.

"You know then. There will be no war party. Wiser heads among us have counselled waiting. It will not be long now before we start on a summer hunt. If we find the Osage on our hunting grounds that will be time enough. Meanwhile practise. There is still much for you to learn."

Black Hawk's heart leaped. Could he possibly mean that next time—no, not yet. Pyesa lifted his hand. Black Hawk knew that he was dismissed. Ketikwe called him.

"Take your small wooden bowl and spoon, my son. There by the fire. The soup has corn and beans the way you like it."

"You pamper him," Black Hawk heard his father grumble.

"He must grow strong," answered Ketikwe. "He must not sicken and die as all our other children have." She turned to her son. "Does it taste well?" Black Hawk nodded as he gulped the food. "Or does it need a nice young rabbit to give it flavor?"

Black Hawk grinned at his mother—wondering a little why his father should chuckle agreeably.

He strolled away, avoiding the other boys. He wandered to the bluff where he drank his fill from the clear, sweet trickle of spring water and hunched down under a tree to brood about how he could hurry his life into the future.

He had been so carefree and happy, ready for any mischief

he and Fox Squirrel could invent. They had daringly explored the caves on Rocky Island, hoping they might actually see the Good Spirit open his huge white wings.

It was only of late that this itch to be a warrior had come upon him. Yet he had not even been sent away to fast and dream so that he might know his destiny. Surely by next summer he would be old enough. He must dream as his great grandfather Manamakee had dreamed, and be a great war chief.

Suddenly Black Hawk sprang up, thrust out his chest and felt his muscles, but immediately sighed in disgust. Jerking his breechclout tighter he started toward the village. So that his parents might not see him, he crept in at the western door of their lodge and took his bow and arrows from underneath his place on the sleeping shelf.

He had started to hunt when he was six. The very first year he had speared a fish. His mother had made a feast in his honor. All the family had praised him. Later he had shot many birds. On winter evenings Pyesa had explained the use of traps and guns.

Once he and Fox Squirrel had wounded a dog and it had to be killed because it was in pain. He had been shamed for his lack of judgment in selecting a target. For punishment they had made him blacken his face and sent him from the lodge. He had not been allowed to eat until his mother had washed his face in the evening.

Now Black Hawk crossed the river in the shallows to one of the islands. Reminding himself of how a Sauk hunter should move, he crept forward silently. He saw a rabbit and impulsively let an arrow fly—far wide of its mark. In chagrin he retrieved it, heard squirrels chattering and moved in their direction.

The light scrabble of their claws as two squirrels chased each other up and down a tree slowed him to quiet watchfulness. Tiring of play they disappeared. Black Hawk waited.

After a time one came into sight on a branch and sat nibbling and smoothing its fur unaware of Black Hawk's presence. He moved closer. The squirrel fixed Black Hawk momentarily with a wary eye. Then, with a whisk of his tail, he was gone.

Still Black Hawk waited. He heard a squirrel chattering, and then he saw it. This one's tail was large and fluffy and the young animal was much absorbed in tending it. Carefully, Black Hawk took aim. The squirrel met the boy's eyes only an instant before the soft whisper of the arrow was upon him.

Black Hawk ran to it. His hand rested on the warm body regretfully. He had laughed in delight at the squirrels' antics when he was a child, but now he was a man, a hunter who must provide for his family.

He frowned, pursed his full lips severely and, detaching the arrow, went on through the forest carrying the squirrel by its tail. It was not long before he stalked home through the village carrying two fat young squirrels.

At his son's coming Pyesa looked up. His head began to nod, and he puffed at his pipe three times in quick succession. Ketikwe, busily pounding a dried buffalo tendon with a piece of flint to make thread, turned and called out in surprise.

Black Hawk held out the squirrels, grinning.

"Would these make the soup taste better, Mother?"

For an instant Ketikwe's hand touched his shoulder.

"My son, some woman will be proud to have you as the hunter for her lodge."

"He who comes in from hunting does not talk with his family until he has eaten," said Pyesa.

"I know, Father," said Black Hawk, and his parents exchanged smiling glances.

"Feed him, then," said Pyesa with an approving grunt.

Black Hawk was still too young to go with the hunting parties when they went out later that summer for deer and buffalo. After the corn was well started, all the tribe had work to do. Black Hawk went with other children and women to

18

fish and gather cattails and reeds for mats. Others stayed home to watch the cornfields.

Late in August all the people were back again in Saukenuk. Crops were coming in and they celebrated the ripening of the corn. Yet at times Pyesa seemed unusually thoughtful and serious in spite of the pleasures of the gambling games he so much enjoyed.

Neither Black Hawk nor Ketikwe understood, but they did know that Pyesa had little use for white men. A trader had been there and perhaps this was the cause of his unusual solemnity.

As the family sat eating Pyesa said, "White men—they are like a spot of raccoon grease on a new blanket. You never can tell how far it will spread."

"We do not see many of them," Ketikwe ventured soothingly, though it was not a woman's place to offer comment or opinion.

Pyesa shook his head.

"As a child I saw none. But now—who can tell how many will come!"

"Oh, but not here—not in our village," said Ketikwe, hastily filling her husband's bowl with the choicest bits left in the kettle.

Black Hawk was puzzled. Surely there was more danger from Osage and Sioux tribes invading their hunting grounds? Why then did his father look so troubled, yet say no more? Was the white man so to be feared?

Black Hawk wanted to ask but did not dare when his father frowned so forbiddingly.

2. *The Dream*

The following spring Black Hawk was fourteen. He sat one day on his heels in front of their lodge, idly scrawling in a patch of bare earth with his forefinger. He gave his mother only half of his attention. He had heard this story many times, but let her talk.

"They had not eaten since the day before so when one of them shot a deer, they immediately stripped off the hide and cut themselves choice pieces. Now they sat around the fire roasting it. It was then it happened.

"They saw her," Ketikwe went on. "The one who has given us corn. A beautiful woman was descending from the clouds and they saw her sit down on the ground some distance from them. She fixed her eyes on the meat, and one of them said, 'She is hungry. Let us give her some of our meat.' The other was agreeable, so one approached her offering a piece of meat."

"She ate it," said Black Hawk. "And then——"

"Every bit of it, and with great pleasure," said Ketikwe, not allowing herself to be hurried. "She ate and then she thanked them very nicely, and said that in one year they must return to this place and they would find themselves and their people greatly rewarded."

"They went home," said Black Hawk, seeing from the corner of his eye that the other boys were signalling him to join them. "And nobody believed a word of their story."

Ketikwe smiled at him.

"Finish it for me."

"When the year passed and they returned they found corn growing where her right hand had rested on the ground, beans where her left hand had been, and tobacco growing where she had sat."

"Good. Go now. Fox Squirrel is waiting for you."

Black Hawk darted away, and the boys headed for the cornfields. There they annoyed the girls who were on watch, or boasted within their hearing of how soon they would be ready to go away to fast and dream. Some of Black Hawk's friends had already dreamed. Surely it would soon be his time, so he too boasted.

Late in the afternoon when he returned to his lodge, Pyesa called Black Hawk to him.

"We have decided. It is time for you to fast and dream that you may know your destiny."

"When?" he croaked, his voice almost failing him.

"You will go tomorrow morning. I have prepared the blackening stick. Tomorrow you will rise before dawn and go to your place."

Black Hawk was restless that night and woke well before daylight. In the darkness he made his way quietly to the river, and grasping an overhanging branch, let himself down into a deep pool. There he thoroughly cleansed himself.

When he returned his father was sitting erect where he had lain down to sleep. Ketikwe did not stir. There was little light, yet he knew that her bright, dark eyes were upon him.

Silently his father handed him the stick of charcoal and watched as he blackened his face. When he finished Pyesa leaned close to peer at him. Then he nodded and motioned toward the door.

"Dream well, my son."

Black Hawk thought he heard Ketikwe murmur, but they spoke no more and he left the lodge. In the soft light of predawn he slipped quietly through the village where no one was astir, and hurried toward the place he had chosen.

He had come upon this hidden glade by accident one day when he had been prowling the woods. It was on the bluff to the east where the forest and the curve of the river gave privacy. Here he could look toward the rising sun, and neither see the village nor be seen by anyone there. Yet he could look far out over the valley to the hills, blue in the distance. Even the smoke rising from a small fire would be lost among the overhanging branches.

Carefully parting the underbrush, he cut away from the trail toward the remembered place. For a moment he was uncertain, then pushed on.

There it was, the cleared, open space. Black Hawk spread his blanket and sat down on it cross-legged, facing east.

The sky brightened. Black Hawk sat quite still so that his Grandfather, the Sun, might gaze on his face and know him as one who was fasting.

All that day he stirred but little from his blanket. He grew weary and restless at times, but the solemnity of the occasion held him quiet. Then he tried to sleep, but the pangs of hunger were upon him and Black Hawk's appetite was enormous. He dozed a little in the warm afternoon sun, but did not dream and he lay there impatiently waiting for night to come.

When the stars glowed in the deepening night, one after the other, he named those he knew. Then, pulling his blanket close, he stretched out and slept the night through with never the least hint of a dream.

The second day began with the sky overcast and sullen. Black Hawk wondered if his dreamlessness would go on and on, if the clouds would blot out the sun. Then his Grandfather could never look on his face long enough to fix it well in mind.

Once, plucking at the grass, his eyes wandering over the

clearing, he saw a plant he knew to be the *bugosk,* the wild
turnip. It did not occur to him that he might dig this up to
eat, or that he might go home and tell them a dream he had
imagined as the old men said some boys did. He could wait.
It would come. It must be a true dream.

In the afternoon he began dancing—round and round he
moved, leaping and chanting all the songs he knew calling
upon his Dream Guardian to come to him.

Exhausted he dropped down on his blanket. He thought
that he saw a black hawk drift across the twilight sky, but
knew he was not dreaming. That night he slept fitfully. Still
he did not dream. He felt he had been awake all night when
he rose and stretched that next morning.

On the third day his mind wandered vaguely from one
thing to another in formless daytime dreaming which he
knew to be no true dream. His body wanted food and he sat
most of that day in a dazed stupor, then he rose in the afternoon and danced until he felt himself lost, weak and floating
somewhere between earth and sky.

When at last he fell asleep, dark thunder heads gathered
upon the horizon.

That night the dream came.

As though tortured, Black Hawk twisted and struggled to
throw off the great power with which he wrestled. They rolled
and tumbled until with a last groaning effort he fought free
and sat upright, only to receive a sharp, violent blow of light
and sound—or so it seemed. Before his eyes, the great tree at
the edge of the clearing was engulfed in flames as the bright
ball of lightning exploded in its branches.

There was the God of Thunder—his protector. It was a
sign, the dream's climax given him in reality, manifesting his
purpose. He would be a great warrior. That was what it
meant.

Feeling spent and weak, Black Hawk touched his face. It

24

was wet. Had it rained during the night or had his dream been so real and fearful that he sweated under its power?

His straying hands touched the blanket and found that it was soaked. Of course it had rained and he had dreamed. The dream was still with him. There before him the tree was burning, its flames diminishing now as dampness smothered the fire.

In awe he thought again—the Great God Thunder had come to him. The god who gave the Sauk men success in war had ordained his future.

He rose to his knees, feeling slightly dizzy at his quick movement, and the dream came back to him again, clear and wonderful. All the signs lingered. The zig-zag of lightning crossed the sky once more—the last of the storm, or was this too a part of his dream? He shivered in fear and wonder.

Before him the east glowed and the rim of the sun appeared. Then directly overhead, brushing so low he could clearly see the bird's fierce eye, a black hawk appeared. It was a sign from the Thunder God.

Black Hawk's legs shook beneath him when he pulled himself upright. He raised his trembling arms upward and thanked the Great Spirit, and stood thus quietly for some moments so that his Grandfather, the Sun, might look upon him again and know him always as one who fasted and was blessed by the Great God Thunder.

Assurance that he would become a great war chief had been given, but he knew too that his stomach felt flat against his backbone. His parents would rejoice that he had dreamed so well. His mother would make a feast for him.

Shakily, Black Hawk made his way down from the high place. Sometimes he doubted that he had dreamed at all. Then again it came back to him strong and clear.

The village was just beginning to stir, but not many were outside their lodges. Black Hawk, his eyes glazed with the dream and his hunger, almost stumbled over a small figure playing in the mud. It was the blue-eyed baby, Keokuk, who stared up at Black Hawk's rain-streaked, blackened face in fright and wonder.

Dropping to hands and knees the child scuttled homeward, bursting into a fit of giggles before he disappeared. Black Hawk's senses sharpened to annoyance. It was an indignity to have his return heralded by giggles and squeaks.

Next spring when the tribe returned to Saukenuk, Black Hawk had turned fifteen. He had grown into a sinewy, lithe young man. The fiercely competitive games were strengthening his muscles and his skill as a hunter had grown during the past winter.

Then, too, though he was not yet allowed to wear paint or feathers, he had gone with his father and a few others on a raiding party against the Osage who constantly ranged north from their lands on the Osage River, a tributary of the Missouri. For the first time he had wounded a man with his lance. His reward for this was to be placed in the lower ranks of the warriors. Soon he could become a waiter to serve the warriors, and when they were on the war path and camped for the night, he would be allowed to stand guard with other young warriors while the older men slept.

He was not yet permitted to go out with a large war party. Often he thought of his dream. Sometimes it was shadowy and he doubted it, only because he had need to prove himself.

Perhaps because of his impatience, Keokuk's pranks were excessively annoying. The child was constantly tagging after the older boys, fixing on Black Hawk as his special target. Pushing in to the center of a group he would stand all puffed up and babbling—pretending that he talked as the chiefs did in council. He of the limber tongue, the boys called him.

Keokuk had even been caught creeping into the council

lodge. With muffled scolding the older boys had dragged him out by the heels.

One day Keokuk burst from the bushes at the side of the trail, whooping and circling around Black Hawk, barring his way. Black Hawk made a menacing gesture, then forcibly set the boy aside, and moved on. He had gone only a step or two before he staggered under the force of the small body flung against him.

Keokuk got his hands under Black Hawk's belt and hung there, dragging behind as Black Hawk tried to shake free of his tormentor. The leather cord that held his breechclout in place gave way. Keokuk fell to the ground with a thud, bursting into a surprised roar that at once dissolved into giggles at sight of Black Hawk stark naked.

Black Hawk snatched breechclout and belt from Keokuk's grasp. He bent to give him a good shaking, but the child rolled out of the way and sprang up, defying him. Black Hawk moved after him with spread palm.

"Go home or I'll——"

Keokuk grinned at him condescendingly, sidestepped out of reach, then skipped off with an air of expecting approval for what he had done.

Black Hawk stared after him, half-smiling, thinking that when he became a warrior of the first grade, when he had killed a man, Keokuk would not dare such tricks.

27

3. Death and A Captive

In September the Sauk left their village for the hunting grounds. With raids and hunting, one winter moon followed another until it was spring again. It was then in his sixteenth year that Black Hawk took his first scalp. This accomplishment allowed him to enter the highest rank of warriors.

He had grown into a handsome warrior, not unusually tall, but broad shouldered, slim hipped, gracefully quick in his movements.

His skin was not as dark as his father's, though face and body darkened in the summer sun. Breechclout and moccasins were gay with red, yellow, and blue porcupine quillwork. The hair was plucked from all his head except the scalp lock. When going with a war party he treated head and scalp lock with vermilion and attached a handsome red-dyed roach of deer hair to the scalp lock, and painted streaks of yellow, blue and red on his face.

Only a string of wampum adorned his neck, as yet no bears' claws necklace. There were three ways to get that—inherit it, trade, or go into enemy country in search of a grizzly, which was risky business but great proof of courage.

Ear bobs rattled and jingled as Black Hawk moved across the central square to join the scalp dance. The prideful way he carried himself drew all eyes. Many a young girl discreetly tried to gain his attention, but he had neither eyes nor thoughts for them. He was bent on becoming a great war chief as the Great God Thunder had predicted.

Before he was seventeen Black Hawk was recruiting his own war parties, as did any warrior whose bravery could command a following. The size of war parties varied, according to their purpose and each war chief's ability to gather men around him. A plentiful supply of game was necessary both for food and clothing, hence they were constantly fighting to protect their hunting grounds.

If a war party took scalps, found itself outnumbered and so retreated, there was no shame in it. A good war leader brought his men home from battle without losing any of them. If an honorable retreat could be managed, it was better to fight another day when conditions were more favorable.

During these years Black Hawk's reputation grew. After leading a party of two hundred warriors in his nineteenth year, he inflicted such losses upon the Osage that they were content to keep away from Sauk hunting grounds, though in earlier years the Osage tribe had ranged far north from the lower Mississippi valley.

With no campaign in sight Black Hawk grew restless. Pyesa noticed this and though he was weary of war and felt his bones beginning to stiffen, he said, "My son, many years ago —you are too young to remember—some of our women and children were murdered by the Cherokee."

Black Hawk put down the arrow head he was making.

"We were hunting to the south. Some of our women went too far in search of roots. The hunting was poor and we needed food."

"It has never been avenged?"

Pyesa shook his head.

"The Osage are quiet now," said Black Hawk. "Isn't it time we did this?"

"Very well," said Pyesa. "I will gather a party."

Pyesa hung a belt of blue wampum painted red in a lodge

apart from the others. Soon men came to touch it and smoke with him. He did not need a large party, thirty was enough to collect a few scalps and thus be avenged.

They travelled south by canoe on the Great River through the tall grass country, lingered around the village of St. Louis for a time, pretending innocence, and sent scouts out in all directions. The scouts returned and came running to leap over the sacred war bundle, the contents of which Pyesa had spread before him. They cried, according to custom, "We have seen the elk feeding along the Meremac."

"Henekohe (all right)," cried Pyesa.

War songs ended, they travelled many miles before they discovered the Cherokee who had moved away from the Meremac below St. Louis. After pursuing them such a great distance they determined to attack, though outnumbered. Pyesa blew his reed whistle, shrill war whoops answered his command, and they rushed upon the enemy.

In the thick of battle, Black Hawk wrenched his lance from the chest of a dying opponent, and saw his father with a great bloody wound torn down his thigh. In that instant before Pyesa fell he swung his club with the strength of a madman. The Cherokee collapsed even as Pyesa fell across him.

The Sauk warriors faltered. Black Hawk, his voice ringing in harsh command, rallied the men. He struck right and left, dodged a lance thrust, swung his tomahawk, and reached his father. There was no chance now to give him aid, or even stoop to see if he still lived. Straddling his father's body, Black Hawk fought off three men, killing two who sought to gain Pyesa's scalp.

At last they forced the Cherokee to retreat into the lengthening shadows of the forest. Black Hawk returned to his father. Panting, his body streaked with sweat and dirt, he knelt and touched the wound, trying to stop the pulsing flow of blood. He knew Pyesa had gone to the Great Spirit. Too much blood had darkened the crumpled grass around him.

31

"It is done," said the *Shaman,* the tribe's medicine man.

Black Hawk nodded, not wanting to speak. With reverence he picked up the sacred war bundle of his ancestors that Pyesa had carried and hung it around his own neck. Then he rose and walked among the fallen men. They had lost seven, the enemy twenty-eight, poor payment for one such as his father.

On his return to Saukenuk the chiefs and elders in council named Black Hawk a war chief, but for five years he joined no war parties. He mourned his father's death and spent his time hunting and fishing for his lodge. At last he felt that the Great Spirit had taken pity on him.

When the crier went about the village calling the chiefs and elders to council he joined the warriors. The Osage were again invading Sauk hunting grounds.

Eager to fulfill the destiny that the Thunder God had promised, Black Hawk led five hundred Sauk and Fox warriors and a hundred Ioway, determined on the extermination of their old enemy. When it was over the Osage stuck to their own territory for a time; and Black Hawk's prestige as a war chief was assured.

The round of seasons passed. It was spring and again the tribe returned to Saukenuk. The corn planted, it was time for the crane dance when young warriors chose their wives.

As often before Black Hawk was twitted because he did not join in. Fox Squirrel had chosen a wife years ago when he first entered his twenties. Black Hawk felt uneasy that there were none among the maidens he wanted.

He brushed aside the joking and soon gathered a small war party, setting out through the tall grass country to avenge the death of his father. At last he came upon four Cherokee men and a child, easily taken—too few to kill for a worthy vengeance.

The child was a skinny little girl of ten or eleven years, with high cheekbones, her black eyes bright and observing. She shrank away from him at first, but when he drew her gently to him and fastened the leading cord around her neck, she submitted without a struggle. All the while he talked to her with words his mother would have used. She seemed unafraid as though she understood the tone if not what he said.

The Cherokee had withdrawn deep into the mountains, too far for his small party to follow. Disgusted, Black Hawk released the four men. They left without a backward glance at the child while she stared after them with a hand pressed against her mouth.

To speed their homeward pace Black Hawk lifted his captive up in front of him on his horse. Reaching home he lingered in the square. The child stood beside him docilely waiting for what would be done with her.

While the men listened to Black Hawk's story, a few half-grown boys came running up. They stared at the girl and then boldly began pulling her hair, demanding that she show her teeth, pinching her arms. She made no motion to defend herself, and stood with dignity.

Keokuk, now a twelve-year old, was among her tormentors. Not daring now to pester the war chief Black Hawk himself, he took special delight in teasing his captive.

"Was this all he found?" exclaimed Keokuk, loud enough to be overheard.

He caught Black Hawk's eye and grinned impudently, but at once veiled his glance. He began to circle the girl, looking at her appraisingly. Eyes downcast, only once did she send a quick, appealing glance up at Black Hawk.

Black Hawk made a threatening gesture, scattering the boys.

"Pay no heed to that one," Fox Squirrel muttered as they walked away.

"He will grow up to make trouble," said Black Hawk. "You shall have this child, Fox Squirrel. She will be a help in your lodge, for your woman is sickly. This one will grow up strong."

Fox Squirrel stopped to look at the girl and said, "What is her name?"

Black Hawk shrugged, and pointing first at himself and then at Fox Squirrel he spoke their names and pointed at her with an inquiring "You?".

She murmured, "Asshewequa."

Thus Singing Bird, Asshewequa, went to live in the lodge of Fox Squirrel, and Black Hawk returned to his fighting— Chippewa, Kaskaskia, and their greatest enemy the Osage, a Siouan tribe.

Again it was time for the corn planting, the feasting, and the crane dance. The young women dressed in their best deerskin garments, gay with brightly colored quillwork, their single braid wrapped in cloth from which long beaded ornaments dangled.

Black Hawk was indifferent to them. If his glance lingered on Singing Bird, no one noticed, nor did he himself wonder why it was that many times his eyes wandered over the people to find her or that he was pleased that she seemed content, well fed, and growing fast. He knew that she was well treated in Fox Squirrel's lodge.

One spring when Black Hawk returned to Saukenuk he was mounted. The raiding party had captured several horses, and Black Hawk, wanting to test his animal's worth had outdistanced his companions. Then too, having a sudden unexplainable desire to reach home, he had taken a short cut.

Almost at the river's edge he realized he was opposite the cornfields and near the place where the women came to bathe. He would have turned and crossed elsewhere but in that instant he heard a girl's angry voice screaming, "Give it to me, give it to me. Go away, I tell you."

Black Hawk urged his horse into the river, scrambled up the opposite bank and, rounding a protruding point of land, came to the bathing place.

A young man lay on his stomach at the edge of the bank, a girl's doeskin dress in his hand. To tease her, he snatched it away and lowered it again just beyond the girl's reach. Apparently she was trying to hide herself in the water and yet rise up far enough to retrieve her garment.

With an angry exclamation Black Hawk struck heels against his horse. He landed on his feet almost before the horse stopped, a pace or two short of the prostrate man. Keokuk leaped up, only an instant before Black Hawk snatched the girl's garment from him.

"What are you doing here? You know it is only for the women."

"The same question goes for you," said Keokuk, with no loss of his composure.

"I've been on a raid. I'd not have come this way, but I heard that girl scream."

"Ah, looking after the girls at last, eh?"

Black Hawk made a half threatening gesture. Keokuk shrugged and sauntered off.

Black Hawk heard a gurgle of laughter. He turned, held out the girl's garment, and looked directly into Singing Bird's eyes. He was startled by her beauty, and his heart leaped as their eyes met. He knew then that the time had come.

Only her head was visible above the grassy bank. As Black Hawk stared, a brown arm appeared and she held out her hand, motioning toward the garment he still held.

"I'm glad you came, Black Hawk. He was making me very angry."

The spell was broken and smiling back at her he said, "He makes me angry too—many times." He tossed the dress down on the bank close to her hand. "Put it on. I will wait for you. Then you can ride home on my new horse."

A few days later Ketikwe, under the shade of a great tree, was working on a deerskin garment, and listening to the festivities of the crane dance. Black Hawk came from the lodge, dressed to take part in the dance and told her he had decided to take a wife. Ketikwe nodded and smiled.

"That is good. I thought you would never come to it. I am getting old. I need small children about me. I need someone to help me with the work of the lodge."

Black Hawk looked at her in surprise.

"But I must go to live with her people—it is the custom."

"Yes," said his mother calmly. "It is the custom, but I have arranged things—the people she lives with do not want you there."

"But Fox Squirrel is my friend——"

Ketikwe lifted her hand.

"Be content. He still is, but their lodge is crowded. He knows that I need you here. If my daughters had lived now there would be sons, hunters, in my lodge. The Great Spirit did not permit that. Fox Squirrel's wife has agreed."

Ketikwe was looking very smug as Black Hawk stared down at her in astonishment.

"You say all this, and you did not even ask the one I have chosen."

Ketikwe folded her blanket close and rocked back and forth, smiling.

"Did you think I did not know who you were waiting for all these years. Yes, I have made the arrangements."

She rose and led him back into the lodge.

"See. I have prepared these things for Singing Bird."

She paused and looked up at him inquiringly.

Black Hawk smiled.

"Yes, it is Singing Bird."

"Here are the clothes I have made. Tonight you can go to her. All is ready."

"But if she does not want me?"

"Ah, then play your flute for her tomorrow—but she will come. I know. She will come."

Ketikwe chuckled and gazed down proudly at the beautiful quilled deerskin garments she had made.

Black Hawk touched her shoulder, and then went forth to the crane dance, already knowing in his heart that Singing Bird would prefer him, a seasoned hunter and warrior.

So according to Sauk marriage custom they became man and wife. Singing Bird came to live in Black Hawk's lodge.

4. A Bad Treaty Brings Bad Times

During the years leading up to 1812 five children were born to Black Hawk and Singing Bird. They were named Little Eagle (Tcuki Keti), Whirling Thunder (Nasheaskuk), Namequa, Blue Jay (Nasomsee), and Swift Flying (Nameakwisa).

There was happiness in his lodge with Singing Bird and the children. Outside in the world around him trouble was brewing. Black Hawk knew this as well as the civil chiefs of many tribes. Year after year they were summoned to Washington for consultation with the Great White Father.

Meanwhile Black Hawk continued to pursue the Osage. Young warriors were not to be restrained. Encountering some of the Osage, it was better to lift a few scalps than to return empty-handed to the jeers of the people. If by chance one or two white men's scalps were among them, what of that. It seemed justified in many cases.

White men could not understand this, nor even why the Indians resented the invasion of their lands both by white settlers and the Osage.

In 1803 the Louisiana Purchase brought Sauk and Fox lands into the hands of the Americans who wanted peace among the tribes. Indians on the war path endangered settlers. Forts were springing up everywhere. The settlers said they needed protection. Thinking of this, Black Hawk spat. Let them stay where they belonged.

Civil chiefs were called into council with the new Governor of the District of Louisiana. The Sauk protested the invasion of the white settlers and asked that the Americans establish a trading post among them as they had asked of the Great White Father in other councils.

Later, the chiefs were again called to Washington and warned that if war came between British and Americans they must remain neutral. British traders would no longer be allowed to come down the Mississippi, but the Americans promised to supply the Indians with goods of high quality.

One day Indians from another Sauk village fled to Saukenuk for protection. A Sauk, when drunk, had killed a white man who had insulted his daughter. The murder seemed justified and they delayed action but finally surrendered the guilty man.

Then a message was received demanding that the chiefs of the village come to St. Louis for a parley with the new Governor. They must bring the guilty Sauk men who had murdered four white people.

Only one man had been killed. Now they were doubtful of justice. Fearing reprisals, many of the people went into hiding, or withdrew to the other side of the Mississippi.

It was finally decided that they must send chiefs to convince the white men that they had already surrendered the guilty man. They would offer to pay for the one killed, thus "covering the blood" spilled, according to Sauk custom.

Four chiefs had been sent: Quashquame, Pashepaho, and two others. Weeks passed. Now at last the chiefs had returned and were making camp outside the village. No-mite, the highest ranking civil chief, had sent a messenger to act as escort.

At the appointed time next day chiefs, elders, and important warriors gathered in the council lodge. Quashquame had been assigned the role of spokesman. With some uneasiness he confessed they had signed a treaty.

Murmuring grew into excited talk. Crouching Eagle called for silence, then turned to Quashquame.

"Say what there is to say—quickly."

Quashquame pulled himself into a semblance of dignity.

"We gave the American Father land—some on the west side of the Great River, and some in the Illinois country opposite the Two Rivers."

"And Saukenuk?" asked Crouching Eagle, his hand lifted.

"No, only from the mouth of the Illinois to the mouth of the Rock River." He hesitated, shifting uneasily. "Not Saukenuk."

"Why did you sign this treaty?" asked Crouching Eagle with such stern authority, the four men seemed to shrink. "Who gave you the right to do this?"

"You were not sent to barter our lands for one murderer," said Black Hawk.

"They pressed us hard," said Quashquame. "They said they would protect us from the Osage."

"What more?" asked Crouching Eagle wearily.

Bit by bit under questioning the full story was told. Shame-faced, they confessed they had been given a great deal of money. None was left. They had been plied with liquor, and fine garments, and they seemed unsure whether they had signed away Saukenuk or not.

"Why did you not tell them only our principal chiefs can sign a treaty concerning our lands?" asked Crouching Eagle.

"We are to have their protection and an annuity," said Quashquame.

"But our land? And Saukenuk?" exclaimed Black Hawk.

"As long as our land remains the property of the Great White Father we are to enjoy the privilege of living and hunting upon it," said Quashquame.

"That does not sound so bad," said Keokuk.

"Privilege," snapped Black Hawk. "On our own land?"

"Take a little now, more later," said Pamaho, who had

41

been among many tribes toward the East. "Then they build forts. What do we gain?"

"A moment of peace, perhaps, for our women," said Fox Squirrel, with a sardonic smile.

"You, Keokuk," said Black Hawk. "Would you trade our land for a little money we shall never see, for a trading post never built?"

"Why do you fume, Black Hawk?" said Keokuk, shrugging his shoulders. "The treaty says we can stay here."

"Does our land mean nothing to you?"

Keokuk was a spectacular war chief, privileged always to ride a horse in battle for bravery he had once shown when riding alone into an Osage camp. Now Keokuk spread his hands and was silent.

"Coward," Black Hawk spat at him. "You would not fight for it?"

At once every man was on his feet.

"There are other ways of getting what one wants from white men," said Keokuk calmly.

"Is that what your white blood tells you?" snapped Black Hawk, and tearing off his own breechclout struck Keokuk across the face with it.

Keokuk's blue eyes widened and a hissing sound came from his clenched teeth. No one spoke in his defense. His pale, angry eyes slid quickly right and left. He knew that Black Hawk, by reason of his exploits in war, was the most respected of the war chiefs. In the lengthening silence he held his tongue.

Black Hawk tied his breechclout in place. Silently all men left the council lodge to form again in small knots about the village.

The next morning Fox Squirrel came to tell Black Hawk that Keokuk had left the village to join the Fox Chief, Powashick.

"Only a coward would desert his village."

"He will be back," said Fox Squirrel.

"Yes." For a moment Black Hawk was silent, then added, "He is young—but he is a Sauk."

Black Hawk shook his head and said no more, thinking: Keokuk the opportunist, the wily one. Wherever he might profit there he would be, but Saukenuk must call him home at times. He was not a white man, in spite of the blue eyes.

They were still hoping for a trading post in 1808 when news came that sent Black Hawk hurrying to his lodge. There Singing Bird was at work repairing mats while she kept an eye on the little three-year-old Nasomsee playing near by.

"I am leaving, Singing Bird," said Black Hawk.

She sprang up and looked at him inquiringly.

"The Americans are building a fort down the Mississippi —above the head of the rapids, the place before we come to our Skunk River hunting grounds."

"Could it be the trading post they promised?" said Singing Bird, her eyes lighting hopefully.

Black Hawk picked up his ball-headed war club.

"We do not trust what they do."

Black Hawk rubbed his shaven head and scowled. A few might be worthy of trust. But what was that when the American chiefs scolded them for fighting other tribes, demanded prisoners be released, that men be punished, and threatened that traders would not be allowed to come among them unless all this was done. And always there was the danger to Saukenuk in that treaty so unwisely signed by the lesser chiefs.

"Will they ever keep the promise?" asked Singing Bird.

"Who knows—but whatever the Americans give us the British give better, and treat us like men." He glanced around the lodge saying, "My sons?".

"Whirling Thunder chases after Little Eagle. They play with Bear Cub and Bee Hunter."

"Good. They will make fine warriors."

43

"Many moons until then."

In a corner the boy Nasomsee had curled up near little Swift Flying, barely out of her cradle board, both asleep. Outside, six-year old Namequa was singing. She was his favorite, Singing Bird sometimes said. If she had been a boy —but then he would not have had the graceful child whose dark eyes lit up at sight of him, just as her mother's did, the child who answered him with such quick perception and who already knew many womanly duties.

"It will only be a few days, no longer," said Black Hawk, content that Singing Bird would see to his children.

He hurried down the trail, thinking of the bad treaty that did this. Forts and settlers following one another—a creeping invasion like water that trickles from a spring, little by little, so that soon all the ground is wet.

The small party of warriors and chiefs travelled several days, then concealed their canoes under low-hanging branches and approached the place quietly.

Crouching Eagle pointed at Appanoose and Pashepaho, saying, "We will counsel with them."

The three chiefs put down their guns, and walked out into the clearing. The rest sought vantage points and peered out from their hiding places, watching. The soldiers outside the stockade stopped their work, then followed the chiefs through the open gate of the stockade and into a building. The gates were not closed and no general alarm went up.

The heavy stockade was at least fourteen feet high. It was obvious to the watchers that the plan was extensive. They had not yet finished hammering and sawing.

At last they saw the chiefs come out the gate. When they reached shelter from prying eyes they made their way back to the others.

"He says Americans keep their promises," said Crouching Eagle. "They are building a trading house."

44

"Why so many buildings then?" asked Black Hawk.

"Soldiers will come to keep the trader company," said Crouching Eagle, his full lower lip bulging as he closed his mouth on that.

"Poor man," said Fox Squirrel. "We could keep him company."

"It will be ready when we go to our hunting grounds," said Appanoose. "The commander says they will have supplies for us as the Great White Father in Washington promised."

"As good as the British give us?" asked Black Hawk.

"They say so," said Appanoose.

"Perhaps they could not do it before," Black Hawk conceded.

"After all, they have been very busy trying to keep us from fighting the Osage," said Fox Squirrel, grinning.

"We will wait and see how well they supply us for the winter hunt, and decide then what we must do," said Black Hawk and all agreed, for they well knew it was fort as well as trading post.

Autumn came. On their way to the Skunk River hunting grounds, women, old people, and children settled into camp in the vicinity of Fort Madison as they had heard the place called. The men went with curiosity and anticipation to the Fort and the stockade gate swung wide to let them in.

They crowded into the trader's building.

"Look at this," said Black Hawk, twisting and pulling at a length of sleazy blue cloth.

"Singing Bird would laugh you out of your lodge if you brought her that!" said Fox Squirrel. "Her old deerskin garments are better and warmer."

Cheap blankets, small amounts of gun powder, rusty guns, battered kettles. They laughed scornfully at the trader, then haughtily gave their names as he accounted for each article.

45

There was nothing they could do then but accept what was offered. The trading house had proved to be but a poor excuse for the Fort.

That winter the chiefs spent many hours mulling over plans. When spring came all able-bodied warriors went into camp some distance from Fort Madison. They did not paint for war, but were all armed with war clubs, bows and arrows, or guns.

Black Hawk and the chiefs watched the Fort for a time. After counselling they decided it would be well to appear friendly, and take in their furs. They were admitted and settled their accounts with the trader. Afterward, they wandered about the enclosure until the officers ordered them out.

Black Hawk slipped around the corner of the stockade, motioning to the others to go on. He moved quietly on moccasined feet, listening, peering through cracks, standing motionless if anyone passed inside. After a short time six men came through the gate, carrying axes and guns and disappeared among the trees.

Soon after they began chopping, Black Hawk heard a loud whooping. Almost immediately the soldiers came running back to the Fort. In the forest, Black Hawk found his warriors convulsed with laughter.

"We crept upon them," explained Fox Squirrel. "They had put their guns down all together. Some of us picked up the guns, others circled them."

Black Hawk grinned for he enjoyed Fox Squirrel's pranks.

"We let out a yell," said Fox Squirrel. "They ran for their guns, saw them in our hands, and all around them Indians, fierce and dangerous."

"Such big eyes, such pale faces," said Appanoose.

"We laughed," said Fox Squirrel, "and gave their guns to them."

They were still laughing when the trader called from near their camp, speaking in their language.

46

"The White Chief says for you to send your chiefs at once to counsel."

"Why should we counsel?" asked Crouching Eagle innocently.

"You know well enough," said the trader. "Send your chiefs or there'll be trouble."

"White men do not like jokes," said Fox Squirrel sadly.

Excitement swept through the camp. Every warrior picked up his weapons. Black Hawk moved among them giving orders.

Chiefs leading, the warriors converged upon the Fort. The gate was opened, the chiefs admitted, and the gate closed against the others.

Old empty barrels and big chunks of wood had been left outside the stockade, the debris of building operations not yet cleared away. The warriors scattered along the stockade, rolling up the big chunks of wood and the barrels to advantageous positions, then climbing up on them to peer over the stockade, calling back and forth.

Near the gate a group began to leap up and down, dancing closer and closer. Black Hawk stood ready to lead the men in. Suddenly a warning came from those who were peering over the stockade. Evidently the white men did not want to be entertained by dancing. Inside, commands were shouted.

The gate was flung open and the chiefs were catapulted out into the midst of the dancing, howling warriors. Black Hawk saw the cannon, aimed and ready, and a soldier running toward it, burning brand in hand. Black Hawk's men scattered without his order.

Their attempt to take the Fort thwarted, they broke camp and started for home. Later when spies brought news that reinforcements had arrived at Fort Madison, a period of uneasy watchfulness began.

The people of all Sauk and Fox villages and of many other tribes became increasingly aware of the invasion of Indian

47

lands. Colonel Dickson, known to the Indians as the Red Head, was a British trader who had come among them often. He brought them goods of high quality, as did other British traders. They encouraged fear of the United States Government, telling the Indians that the Americans plotted to take their lands from them.

An emissary from the Shawnee came to the village urging chiefs and people to unite with the Shawnee and all tribes in a great war against white people. No promises were given in Saukenuk.

Black Hawk, Fox Squirrel and Atako lingered in the square after he had gone.

"This might be the time to do what he asks," said Black Hawk thoughtfully.

"But all the tribes?" exclaimed Fox Squirrel. "It would never work. The Osage and Sioux have been our enemies for too many years."

"Our people do not want to go," said Appanoose, joining them. "Perhaps some time, but not yet."

The group broke apart and Black Hawk, still troubled, sought comfort with his family.

Late that afternoon, Colonel Dickson came to his lodge. He brought presents and spoke disparagingly of the Shawnee visitor.

"Pay no attention to him, Black Hawk. He is a trouble-maker. He only wants to spoil our fur trade with you."

He talked with Black Hawk for some time. In the end, he only added to Black Hawk's uneasiness.

"Will you eat now?" said Singing Bird, coming into the lodge after the Red Head had left.. He nodded. "You are troubled, husband?"

"I keep remembering what the Shawnee visitor said."

She waited, wooden spoon held above the bowl of thick soup.

As though deep in his own thoughts Black Hawk went on.

48

"He said to us: 'If you do not join your friends on the Wabash, the Americans will take this very village from you.' "

Singing Bird's hand shook so that she spilled some of the soup. Black Hawk touched her shoulder.

"Ah, do not waste the good soup. Do not be afraid, Singing Bird. I will not let them take our village."

He smiled then and drew the children around him, but he knew that Singing Bird watched him with troubled eyes. For a woman she had a curious way of divining all that went on in his mind.

5. Forced Into War

In June of 1812 civil chiefs from the Sauk, Fox, Osage, Sioux, Winnebago, and Ioway tribes were taken to Washington to counsel with the Great White Father, who hoped to keep them friendly to Americans and neutral in case of war between Britain and America. Black Hawk, meanwhile, set out to track down the truth about the rumors of war between the two countries.

He visited Peoria on the Illinois River but Thomas Forsyth, a trader he had once met and trusted, was absent, nor did he learn anything at the friendly Potawatomi villages. The answer awaited him in Saukenuk.

Colonel Dickson was there and came to the point at once. The Americans had declared war upon the British. Now he asked help from his Indian friends.

As he talked the Red Head began pulling rolls of gay cottons, knives, kettles, ribbons and a pile of blankets from his boat, spreading them out invitingly.

Black Hawk fingered a heap of ear bobs and then stroked a blanket with red stripes, thinking how it would become Singing Bird. Without seeming to do so, he counted the blankets and said, "The British have always been good to us. I have not discovered one good trait in the Americans who have come among us."

"Then you will join us?" said the Red Head in his burring Scotch-Irish voice.

"I can decide nothing. The chiefs are in Washington."

"You are their great war chief. You can decide."

"We must counsel," said Black Hawk, knowing the chiefs would take his advice, but unmoved by the flattery.

Black Hawk took his presents to the lodge. As he left, heading for the bluff where he could look down on the river and be undisturbed, Singing Bird was stroking her blanket, saying, "By this they gain much favor with the Great Spirit."

Caught in the tug of war going on between Americans and British, used for their intrigues and deceptions, Black Hawk was being forced toward a decision. Misunderstanding white men's ways, almost entirely ignorant of their language, he struggled to preserve things valuable to his people.

There on the bluff he weighed the problem. Certainly, he would not fight for the Americans. The British made few promises, but he could rely on them. If he joined any side at all, it must be the British—but why should he fight white men's wars?

Yet, if they fought well for the British, they might be able to drive out the Americans. Then Saukenuk—this place of happiness for his people—would be in danger no longer. Here he had discovered how beautiful and right Singing Bird had become for him, so that he wanted no other wives. Here rested the bones of his ancestors. His own must lie beside them.

He thought again of the time they had helped Winnebago friends attack Fort Madison to revenge the killing of their chief. His mouth turned down in disgust. His fire arrows had failed. He had shot through the rope that held the flag, but they ran it up again. Then their ammunition had given out.

Returning home, they had brought with them the broken body of Fox Squirrel. The Shaman and the women had brought him back to life. Dragging a maimed leg Fox Squirrel crept about the village, but he would never ride or hunt again—he who had ridden gaily away on any adventure, he who had whooped and clowned for them and yet had stood fast in battle.

Now Black Hawk struck his thigh in troubled indecision. If the British drove the Americans out of Fort Madison, it would avenge Fox Squirrel.

Then he put all these thoughts from him when he saw the ten-year old Namequa spring like a young doe up the rise of ground. He held out his arms to receive her.

It was a hopeful party that set out from Saukenuk that autumn, eager to begin the hunt as soon as they had received supplies. While the women set up camp Black Hawk and the other men, wrapped in their ragged blankets, presented themselves at Fort Madison. They smoked and ate, and then rose to shake hands with a strange trader. They waited, grew impatient, and asked for their supplies. They did not understand the delay.

The strange trader called for the interpreter, Maurice Blondeau. He explained they were not to receive anything until spring. Angry talk grew loud. Black Hawk silenced them and spoke.

"The Great Father in Washington promised our chiefs you would supply us. The Great Father speaks the truth, so you must give what is promised—*now*, when we are greatly in need."

Still the refusal was repeated. Pulling dignity and shabby blankets around them, Crouching Eagle and Black Hawk led the men out.

"A good hunt! With an empty gun or none at all," grumbled Crouching Eagle. Calling Quashquame to him, he said, "Are you sure you understood the White Father in Washington?"

"I am sure. They did not give us liquor if that——"

"The interpreter made it very plain," Pashepaho interrupted. "Goods were promised us *before* we went to the hunting grounds."

"I feared this," said Black Hawk.

Their gloom was dispelled in the morning. A messenger came down river to tell them that LaGuthrie, a British trader, had just reached Saukenuk with presents from the British.

They hurried back home. Next day, when the presents were being divided, LaGuthrie drew Black Hawk aside. He motioned toward the sound of women's squeals of laughter and delight.

"See, Black Hawk, how good the British Father is to your people," he said, speaking in Black Hawk's own language.

"We are happy. You have saved our people by giving us supplies for the hunt."

"Now listen, Black Hawk. The Red Head wants you to raise a party of two hundred men."

Black Hawk gave him a sharp glance, then said, "Our chiefs have promised the Americans we would stay at peace."

"Why should you keep the promise when they treat you badly?"

Black Hawk shrugged.

"The Red Head has twelve boat loads of goods, guns, and ammunition waiting for you in Green Bay."

Enough to clear out all the whites around Saukenuk, thought Black Hawk. It was tempting.

"The Red Head said: 'Tell Black Hawk, if you do not immediately strike the Americans I will turn all the other Indians against you and strike you to the ground.'"

"He wants us to attack the settlements?"

"Not yet. First get the two hundred warriors and join him at Green Bay."

Still smarting under American betrayal, Black Hawk hesitated no longer.

"I will raise the war party," he said.

He had no trouble gathering two hundred warriors from his own and other Sauk and Fox villages. Crouching Eagle, a civil chief, felt that he must stay with the people. Keokuk smoothly refused, saying, "I will wait here and see what is best for our people to do."

That winter of 1812-13 Black Hawk and his followers fought well, but they had no stomach for a long siege. That was not the way they conducted wars, hence small parties of his warriors were continually drifting off toward home.

In early August of 1813 the British were defeated on the lower Sandusky in Ohio. Ordered to draw back, Black Hawk and his warriors reformed some distance from the British. Black Hawk called Pamaho to him.

"The Americans fight better than we thought," said Black Hawk as he carefully undid the flaming red crest of deer hair from his scalp lock, and tucked it away in the pouch at his belt. "I have had enough of these British. I long to return to Saukenuk."

Pamaho glanced in the direction of the scattered British troops, watching as a doctor moved among them ministering to the wounded and dying.

"Atako and Pashepaho feel the same," he said. "We have had no plunder. What sort of a war is this?"

"Pass the word among us. You know that hillock just beyond the bend of the river—where we camped?"

"I know."

"Meet there tonight."

Twenty warriors joined Black Hawk and slipped away in the darkness. There were many miles to go and much of it was strange country. Summer was on the wane before they reached the tall grass prairies. There, on the Illinois River in Potawatomi lodges, they were welcomed and given food, pipes, and gossip. But they learned nothing of what had happened in Saukenuk. They travelled on for three more days before Black Hawk said, "We will be home by sunset."

One of the men called out, "Look—smoke."

Black Hawk sent his warriors on home and went to investigate. Pushing his way through undergrowth where there was but scant trail, he reached the shelter of sumach bushes. Through the branches he could see an old man seated beside a small fire, which gave off more smoke than heat. A mat tied between two saplings provided scanty shelter from the sun.

Someone had come here to humble himself before the Great Spirit. Black Hawk stepped back, not wanting to intrude. There was something familiar about the humped figure, however, that troubled him. He hesitated, looking back.

Then quietly, he drew near and seated himself beside the old man. Glazed eyes, resting on Black Hawk momentarily, seemed only to know that someone sat beside him.

"Fox Squirrel, it *is* you?" said Black Hawk.

Hastily lighting his pipe he put it between Fox Squirrel's lips.

"What are you doing here alone? Where is your son?"

The old man cringed, but eagerly drew a few puffs on Black Hawk's pipe. When he looked at Black Hawk again he seemed to recognize him, but did not speak. His head drooped lower and lower.

Black Hawk hurriedly seized an empty bowl lying nearby and ran to the brook. When he held the water to Fox Squirrel's lips saying, "Drink, my friend, drink," the old man gulped the water down, his scrawny throat contracting with the effort. Leaning heavily against Black Hawk he gasped, "You are home at last."

"Yes, home. Tell me, what of Saukenuk and our people, and your son?"

How Fox Squirrel had changed. In these few moons he had become an old, old man. Now he spoke in a thin child's voice.

"You left. I went to Salt River. They had built a Fort. The war chief said I could hunt on the Illinois side of the Mississippi. We were content—good hunting, game plenty."

His head nodded. Black Hawk forced another drink between his lips.

"Two moons there," said Fox Squirrel slowly. "My boy went out to hunt. In the morning, my woman roused the other lodges—they could follow his trail—snow on the ground. They found him——"

The tears ran helplessly from the old man's sunken eyes. Black Hawk waited. Fox Squirrel continued.

"They found the deer he had shot, hung in a tree. Tracks of white men. My son was a prisoner. They followed. Near the Fort they found him. Murdered. His arms tied behind him, his body stabbed, scalped——" The old man turned piteous eyes to Black Hawk. "His face was all shot to pieces."

Black Hawk raised his fist above his head and shook it in rage, while Fox Squirrel sniffled and moaned beside him.

The sky darkened and Black Hawk saw storm clouds gathering. Thunder muttered, drawing closer, and the wind brushed over them. The Great Spirit too was angered.

Black Hawk wrapped the old man in his own blanket, took his hand and said, "Be comforted. I will avenge him."

After a moment Fox Squirrel said, "I am alone. My woman died of grief on our way up the Mississippi."

The storm broke over them. Black Hawk sheltered his friend as best he could. Thunder rumbled away into the distance, and finally there was only the drip of water from leaf to leaf. Black Hawk eased the old man against a tree, hoping he slept.

It took some time to make a fire. When at last it burned

and he had nursed it into a little warmth, he turned again to Fox Squirrel. Touching him he knew that the Great Spirit had come for Fox Squirrel while his back was turned.

Black Hawk wrapped the blanket around him with tender care and, unable to sleep, awaited the dawn. When the first light touched the sky some of the warriors returned. Black Hawk looked up at his men.

"Fox Squirrel is dead."

"We will help you bury him," said Pamaho, sadly.

When it was done as Black Hawk directed, they went home.

Chiefs and a large party of the elders came to receive them. Crouching Eagle, Appanoose, Quashquame and Wakome, the Old One, all greeted Black Hawk formally and escorted him to a lodge on the central square. Such a reception cheered his spirit. A quick glance over the women and children crowding the square and he felt a sinking within him. Where was his family?

When he was seated on the buffalo robes with the other chiefs and head warriors around him in the lodge, food was served him by one of the young warriors.

Black Hawk took the bowl of soup, thick with meat and beans and ate hungrily as the others watched in courteous silence. It was good. Surely no hand but Singing Bird's had prepared it. He put down the empty bowl. At once, pipes were lit and passed around. After a few puffs, he said, "Now I will tell you all that has happened to me."

He spoke then in detail of the attack on Frenchtown, of the long days of idleness around Detroit, of the different forts, of the bravery of his men, and why, at last, he had decided to leave the British. He related that both sides fought well, and that the Americans were fine soldiers.

"They shoot better than the British," he said. "But we would not follow a chief who fights as the white men do. We believe it is wise to kill the enemy and save our own men.

They march right out into the open and keep right on fight-ing—no matter how many they lose."

"There would be none left to care for our women and children if we did that," said Crouching Eagle.

Then Black Hawk told them how they feasted and drank after the battle was over. He had heard, too, that each side then wrote statements telling how they had won the battle.

Though the listeners wanted more, Black Hawk was anxious for news of the village and of his family. They told him of the rumors of danger to Saukenuk and it was plain these fearful men had been at a loss without their war chief. There were few able warriors in the village.

They had decided they must cross the Mississippi. As one began to tell how Keokuk had then spoken, Black Hawk could almost hear that smoothly eloquent voice. The elders had been relieved by his bombastic assurance. They were glad to permit him to gather the few warriors he could, send out spies, and march off to protect their village. He had found no Americans. Saukenuk had not been assaulted by anyone.

"And where is this Chief Keokuk now?" asked Black Hawk, his voice deceptively mild.

"He has gone to St. Louis," said Quashquame. "To see the Americans."

"To discover what they wish him to do now, I suppose."

Appanoose and old Wakome stirred uneasily.

Abruptly Black Hawk laughed and said, "Keokuk took the necessary precautions. I am satisfied."

Black Hawk rose and the others followed his example. At the doorway he said, "My family?"

"They are here now," said Crouching Eagle.

Singing Bird was nowhere in sight as he approached his lodge. He pursed his lips and gave the evening song of the hermit thrush with which he had always signalled her. Her answer came at once.

He went swiftly in. There was Singing Bird, standing just

aside from the doorway, her eyes dark and soft, her clasped hands pressed against her breast. The children, all of them, Little Eagle, Whirling Thunder, Namequa, Nasomsee and the smallest one, Swift Flying were just behind her.

"I have eaten," he said, and held out his arms.

Singing Bird and the children closed in on him. Only Little Eagle stood aside, a bit stiff and serious, for he had just turned fifteen, but it warmed Black Hawk's heart to meet the speaking eyes of his first-born son.

"They have told you all?" asked Singing Bird.

"Part of it."

"We had to go with Quashquame. So many of us were without food. They took us to a safe place on the Missouri River. The Americans thought we were a part of the Peace Band."

"We could not bear to stay away from Saukenuk," said Whirling Thunder.

"When the birds started north we too had to go," said Swift Flying.

Singing Bird let her hand rest on Swift Flying's head and said to Black Hawk, "Keokuk would have defended us if necessary. He has an agile tongue. He might have persuaded the Americans we were the peaceful band."

"Quite right—perhaps he did," said Black Hawk. "But that is past. The danger is ahead for us."

"What danger?" Singing Bird asked anxiously.

"Our people are being torn apart—scattered."

"What will happen to Saukenuk?"

Wearily shaking his head, Black Hawk left that unanswered and said, "I must rest now, Singing Bird. They have told you of Fox Squirrel?"

She nodded, and her hand tightened on his arm before she let him go.

6. *A Treaty Signed But Not Accepted*

Black Hawk rode off taking Neapope with him to avenge the death of Fox Squirrel's son. Though young, Neapope was a chief by inheritance, and so was admitted into council with the older chiefs. His long straight nose and high cheekbones, in the broad face with its high forehead, gave him a look of maturity, to which the sullen mouth added a somber thoughtfulness. His youthful enthusiasm and unconcealed admiration for the older chief had caught Black Hawk's attention.

When they returned with a few scalps he was satisfied with Neapope, but other things gave him small comfort. Many of the lodges had yielded to Keokuk's persuasiveness and left for Portage des Sioux to join the Peace Band under the protection of the Americans, Pashepaho among them.

Hunting was neglected or left to the older men and boys that winter. Black Hawk and the warriors travelled about the country to discover what was going on between the British and Americans.

By the following spring many of the Potawatomi had made peace. Back in Saukenuk too, the news was bad. The Americans were building a fort at Prairie du Chien, up the river.

Saukenuk settled into its summer routine. Black Hawk spent long afternoons talking and feasting, or teaching Little Eagle and Whirling Thunder tricks of riding, as they tore at full gallop across the prairie. Both boys, now sixteen and

63

fifteen, had dreamed and were eager to advance into the ranks of the warriors.

One day there was a great hullabaloo of barking dogs and screaming children. Visitors, riding into the village, presented a glorious sight on their prancing horses, gay with feathers and dangling ornaments.

"Keokuk comes like the chief of a nation," said Neapope.

"The Americans think he is," said Black Hawk. Smiling he went forward with the other chiefs to welcome his rival.

He could not suppress a twinge of anger when he saw that Pashepaho and Ahnowa rode with him. Nor did he fail to notice as Keokuk dismounted that his gaily decorated horse dripped blood from where spurs had gouged his sides.

Keokuk was courteously received, though many of the people turned away. A feast was prepared for the guests and after the men had smoked with him, Keokuk began to talk.

"My brothers, I have come to bring you news of our people. They are living well, and are at peace with the Americans. There is good hunting on the Missouri. Many Potawatomi as well as Sauk and Fox have gathered under the Americans' protection. The British are not winning their battles. Do you not think it wise then to make peace? The Americans will be glad to have you on their side."

"No doubt," growled Crouching Eagle.

Keokuk went calmly on as if he had not heard.

"I have listened. I have grown to know the English language. They think they can talk without my understanding— but I understand."

"You do not understand your own people," said Neapope, "if you think we would bow our necks to the murdering Americans."

"Let Keokuk have his say," said Black Hawk, gesturing the young man to silence.

Keokuk acknowledged this with a courteous bow. He talked

64

on saying finally, "It would be well to have the Americans look on us with favor. If they defeat the British what will become of you then?"

Black Hawk fingered his pipe, thinking that, in such a case, was it not better to choose the way Keokuk offered—compromise and toady? He hesitated. How could he be so sure that the British would lose? One battle or two was not a war. If there was any hope for Saukenuk, it lay with the British.

"Does our village of Saukenuk mean nothing to you, Keokuk?" said Black Hawk, his voice deceptively mild.

Keokuk shrugged.

"There are other places as good. I have seen them."

Black Hawk rose, and stood looking down at Keokuk.

"Then go and look at them again and do not come to us with talk of protection from the Americans. Give them what they want, they only take more."

Keokuk looked up at him insolently.

"I intend to keep them in my debt. They will think me a great leader of our people."

Black Hawk stalked from the lodge, unmindful of the murmuring around him. Once more he had been stung by Keokuk's insolence breaking through his sly pretense of respect for an older war chief—all the more obviously pretense now that he stood so well with the Americans.

Despite rebuffs, Keokuk and his warriors lingered into July, urging the people to treat the Americans whenever they passed on the river without signs of anger.

When American boats were sighted a few days later, Black Hawk said, "Keokuk will want to meet this war chief when he comes."

"He left this morning—well before dawn," said Neapope.

"Ah, he would not want to be counted with us."

Black Hawk picked at the baubles hanging from his ear, regarding the messenger before them thoughtfully.

"How many boats and soldiers?"

"Five or six boats. A hundred men, perhaps more. We saw them go aboard."

"It might be well to counsel," said Black Hawk. "Let them think we are peaceful."

On his arrival, Major Campbell was greeted by a white flag. When his party landed to parley a hundred and fifty warriors gathered. Black Hawk and the chiefs had passed word among them—no weapons, and appear friendly.

Black Hawk sat quietly during the council. He had to admit to himself that Keokuk's talk had made an impression. He would watch and wait. The Sauk chiefs were amiable, agreeing to all suggestions.

The American war chief seemed satisfied and anchored his boats. That night spies brought word that the British had taken the fort at Prairie du Chien. Thus encouraged Black Hawk attacked and, in the end, aided by the British and stormy weather, came off the victor.

Word spread that the Americans were building up a great force to overcome Saukenuk. The Indians began to gather for its defense.

Only a few of the Sauk Peace Band remained docilely on the Missouri after that. Many had come home. Now others in the Sauk and Fox villages felt with Black Hawk that the Americans could be driven out. All that fall, small raiding parties swept up and down the Mississippi, until finally the building of Fort Johnson at the mouth of the Des Moines River was abandoned.

Captain Bulger, the British commandant at Fort McKay, Prairie du Chien, was giving many presents to the Indians that winter. Colonel Dickson, the Red Head, also was generous with supplies, seeking out Black Hawk in the Two Rivers country hunting grounds of the southeast Missouri region.

Well before sugar making time, Captain Bulger summoned the Indians of many tribes to Prairie du Chien. Nearly twelve hundred gathered there. Black Hawk, far afield with his warriors, was not present. On his return to Saukenuk he stood in the square talking with the chiefs.

"The British have not made peace," said Neapope. They promised that our Great Father, the King, will help us."

"You have proof of this?" asked Black Hawk.

"They told us that great fleets are arriving in Quebec. The Americans are being attacked again."

Someone near the river called to them. A boat was coming to shore.

"Our British comrade has come," said Black Hawk recognizing one of their visitors.

The chiefs hastened to shake Lieutenant Graham's hand with great formality. He ate and smoked with them. Then Black Hawk and the chiefs listened as the interpreter told them the British would keep on fighting until their lands were restored to them.

"That is the promise," said Graham, urging the interpreter to repeat what he had said, and adding, "We urge you, we strongly urge you to begin your raids on the Mississippi settlements once again."

No-mite was about to send someone to silence a disturbance outside when Black Hawk's keen ears caught a word or two. He sprang up as a messenger burst in.

"The Americans—that boat, *Clark,* it is here, carrying a white flag."

Graham leaped to his feet, exclaiming, "The *Clark?*"

The Indians stared at him suspiciously. Then, as one man, they headed for the river. Here they found the *Clark's* commander looking about uneasily. The two white men saluted each other smartly, and there was a quick exchange of talk. Black Hawk looked from one to the other.

"This is true?" asked Graham.

"On my honor as an officer of the American Army," said the commander. "The Treaty of Ghent was signed in December (1814). Official news has just reached us."

"And I came down here to get Black Hawk to go to work on you again," said Graham ruefully.

Black Hawk thrust a forefinger at the interpreter.

"What news is this? Tell us."

Graham turned to the interpreter.

"Tell Black Hawk: *do not go to war.* The Americans and the British have made peace. I must return at once. My God —we've got war parties going out." He looked directly at Black Hawk. "Promise me this, Black Hawk. *You must not go to war.*"

He waited until the interpreter had finished.

"Any promises I make, I keep," said Black Hawk. "Now I make no promises. I am not like you. Your promises mean nothing."

Graham lifted his hands helplessly.

"Tell Black Hawk the war is over. There is nothing I can do but obey the orders of my war chiefs."

Hastily he saluted the American commander and lifted his hand in a gesture of peace to the Sauk. When the *Clark* too had left, there was furious talk.

By early May more than eight hundred angry Indians camped around Fort McKay at Prairie du Chien. They milled about, gathering in groups to discuss the failure of the British. Saukenuk chiefs greeted the Red Head with solemn faces. They heaped their blankets and saddles together so he might stand a little above them when he spoke.

"My red children," he began. "I am bowed down in sorrow that I must leave you. There is nothing I can do. The great war chiefs of the two countries have made peace. The Americans will not allow me to stay here. I must go far away to the Red River country. I am filled with gloom that I am forever to leave my much-loved red children."

They came to shake his hand and wept unashamedly as they

bade him farewell. They were not afraid to let him know how they mourned his departure.

On the tenth of May, Captain Bulger called the principal chiefs of the many tribes into council. Black Hawk listened carefully to the interpreter. Talk, talk—white men in council were worse than Indians.

When the chiefs spoke and his turn came Black Hawk dropped his blanket and, in the pride of his near-naked war dress, stood commandingly before the white war chief. Lifting the war belt of wampum, he held it high above his head, shaking it before the stern faces of the British commanders.

"Now hear this, our British Father. You have given us promises you do not keep. I have fought the Long Knives, the Americans, and will continue to fight them 'til they are off our lands. Until then, my Father, your red children cannot be happy. I am done."

Neapope followed Black Hawk from the council as did the others of their band.

On the homeward trail with Neapope at his side, Black Hawk could not shake off his sadness or his silence. At length Neapope said, "Those were brave words you spoke."

"Brave words with little meaning. I spoke in anger."

Neapope eyed him speculatively.

"You could gather the tribes."

"The time may come for that—but not now," said Black Hawk. "See how the tribes scatter."

"They scatter, but they will raid as they go. The settlements will not sleep easily."

Black Hawk smiled, and touched his horse so that the animal pranced in response.

"You tempt me," he said.

Neapope glanced back at the civil chiefs following them and said softly, "You gave warning to the white men."

Black Hawk did not stay long in Saukenuk after their return, but gathered a war party as many others were doing.

69

Afterward, on the way home across country, he decided they had accomplished nothing. Scalps had been taken but good warriors lost did not rid them of the Americans. They had gained several horses scattered by gunfire and stolen from settlements, but that was all.

As they approached the village Black Hawk, leaving his companions, turned toward the river. Plunging into the water, splashing and rubbing with sand, he rid himself of war paint and the filth of their journey. Cleansed, he climbed up the river bank.

His sons were there admiring their father's new addition to the tribe's growing herd of horses. He acknowledged their presence with a nod and grunt. With Little Eagle and Whirling Thunder leading the horse and carrying his equipment, he started for home.

Behind him Little Eagle spoke.

"I have killed a deer, Whirling Thunder. Some of it is roasting now."

"I ate of the soup," said his brother. "It is good—very good. Our father will like it."

Black Hawk smiled, but did not turn to them. His step quickened. Singing Bird would be waiting for him.

When he crossed the central square No-mite and Appanoose called to him, and he sent his sons on to their lodge.

"The British have left Fort McKay burning and are gone," said Appanoose when Black Hawk joined them.

Black Hawk spat into the dust.

"I have said I would do what I could to prevent war," quavered No-mite.

"It is no good now to fight either Americans or British," said Black Hawk. "I am done with it, but there is much anger among the young warriors."

"For me, it has come to this, Black Hawk," said Appanoose. "I have decided to take my band and join those on the Missouri."

"I cannot stop you," said Black Hawk sadly, turning away.

"Wait," said No-mite. "Yesterday a messenger came. The Americans have summoned us to a council at Portage des Sioux, above St. Louis."

"Does Keokuk say we must go?"

"I have not seen Keokuk for many moons—he stays on the Missouri," said Appanoose.

"Gathering what lodges from us that he can."

Appanoose avoided his eyes, but said, "It is my own decision."

"A man must do what he thinks best," said Black Hawk, and for a moment the three friends were silent. Old No-mite sighed wearily.

"There is no hurry to go to this council."

The time for their appearance at Portage des Sioux passed. Then Nicholas Boilvin, interpreter and agent for the Americans, came to them. It took three days of talking, but it was finally decided someone must go.

"I myself will go," said No-mite. "As soon as Wapello comes."

With Wapello, principal chief of the Fox and others of his tribe joining the Sauk people, the party set out down the Great River. It was mid-afternoon when No-mite groaned and fell forward, retching and vomiting.

"I am sick, bad sick," he moaned as the other canoes drew abreast.

"We must stop," said Crouching Eagle to Tiamah, No-mite's brother. "He cannot stand this journey."

"If we paddle fast we can reach the village on the Henderson River," said Black Hawk. "They have a Shaman."

There the party was welcomed, and the next morning the men stood around the lodge where the Shaman worked his charms with No-mite.

"We must go on," said Wapello. "We can tell them what has happened, that the Sauk are coming soon."

They left and two more days passed before Tiamah tottered forth from the lodge to tell them No-mite had died. Tiamah, now the head chief and almost as old as his brother, refused to go on. Since the Sauk could not talk of treaties without their principal chief, they returned to Saukenuk. Then, too, respect for a chief demanded his proper burial.

The summer was well gone before Wapello and the others returned. They reported that the Americans were angry and would not listen to their explanation. They threatened to send a war party against the Sauk. Black Hawk laughed at that, saying, "They would not dare."

"There are no British to help you this time," said Wapello.

Black Hawk knew the truth of this and was silent.

"Appanoose told them you would never give up Saukenuk," said a young Fox chief.

"Then the American chief's face grew very red," said Wapello.

"Appanoose was there?" asked Neapope.

"He signed with the Missouri Peace Bands."

"And Keokuk?" said Black Hawk.

"Oh yes," said Wapello.

Springing up, he thrust out his chest and strutted back and forth, mimicking Keokuk's manner. "The Americans think he is a very great chief among us."

"They give him and his wives many presents," said a young chief.

"His very skin is turning white to go with his blue eyes," said Wapello, half sullen, half envious.

Boilvin was the Americans' Indian agent and interpreter in Prairie du Chien that winter. Earlier, in St. Louis, the Sauk had known him as a friend. He visited their hunting grounds and at length gained a promise. They would go to St. Louis in the spring and sign the treaty the Americans required.

In May, 1816, Black Hawk made his mark upon a treaty he did not trust or fully understand.

The Indians filed out of the room, Black Hawk among the first for he longed to find some place that he might hang his head in shame, unseen.

A smiling Keokuk shouldered his way to Black Hawk.

"I am glad you came. I am sure you will soon believe that it is well to do this."

"It is the first time I have touched goose quill to paper. I cannot be happy that I submit to the Americans."

"The Americans will be good to us. Many think so. Wapello agrees with me too." Keokuk puffed up his chest and tugged at his bears' claws necklace and gabbled on. " . . . I have made friends among them. Forsyth, the agent, thinks well of me. I too can return to Saukenuk."

Black Hawk was silent. The crowd pressed on them and the two men allowed themselves to be separated. From a corner of his eye Black Hawk saw that Wapello was following Keokuk. Wapello, who had once scoffed at Keokuk's vanities and mimicked him cruelly, now wished to be on his side.

The American flag snapped briskly in a crisp wind that suddenly blew chill against Black Hawk's heart. He straightened, pulled his blanket closer, and hastened to be gone.

7. Trouble in Saukenuk

The Sauk chiefs paddled toward home. A few miles below Saukenuk Little Eagle and Whirling Thunder awaited them, bringing news that a fort was being built on Rocky Island.

Later that day the chiefs stood on the bluff overlooking the Island. Several buildings were under construction on the high, rocky west end. One, its lower part of stone, had an appearance of permanence.

They turned as Keokuk rode up with a flourish and jumped down from a winded, heaving horse.

"Do they plan to fight us?" asked Crouching Eagle.

"You have just signed a peace treaty," said Keokuk. "It is not likely—but they will want us to move beyond the Mississippi."

"We made no such promise," snapped Black Hawk.

"This treaty you have just signed——"

"We signed because we had to sign," said Black Hawk. "The Great Spirit gave us this land years ago. A touch of the goose quill cannot change that."

He leaped onto his horse and rode off. Within his lodge he found Singing Bird bending over the nine-year old girl, Swift Flying, who lay whimpering and restless close to the fire.

"She says she is cold, then hot," said Singing Bird.

"Is it bad, little one?" asked Black Hawk, touching her cheek. Swift Flying cuddled up to him and at once seemed more content, her eyelids drooping. A strange way for the lively one to act.

"Do you think it would be well to get the Shaman to drive out this Bad Spirit?"

"No, I have given her a drink from the herbs I brewed. When she wakes, the fever will be gone."

"Ah yes, what need have we for a Shaman. You take good care of my children."

Black Hawk sighed and stretched out beside his child.

The officers at Fort Armstrong on Rock Island were aware of the Sauk's displeasure and, as a pacifier, brought kegs of rum to the village. Having a little, the young men wanted more. The elders did not like to see their warriors lying in sodden unconsciousness when they should be hunting or playing at the traditional games and dances, perfecting their skills.

Nor could anyone go far from the village without encountering white men. The young warriors ranged over the prairies garnering a scalp or two in lonely settlements. Where white people felt themselves the stronger, a lone Indian was in trouble too.

Neapope and Black Hawk stood in the central square one day discussing these things.

"Look!" suddenly exclaimed Neapope, pointing.

Black Hawk whirled around. Little Eagle was riding toward them. Blood streamed from face, shoulders, and chest. He breathed in great, wrenching gasps and friends, riding on either side, supported him.

"My son, my son, what has happened?" cried Black Hawk.

"He cannot speak, Father," said Whirling Thunder. "Too difficult to breathe—he gasps——"

Willing hands reached to help. Little Eagle was eased down from his horse. His legs doubled under him and he would have sunk to the ground had he not been supported. Someone brought a blanket. Gently they laid him on it.

Singing Bird pushed through the crowd. Her hands ran

swiftly over her son's head, back, and shoulders. She did not even respond to Black Hawk's anxious questions as he knelt beside her. This was woman's work.

"To the lodge, quick," cried Singing Bird.

Four young men on either side held the blanket tight, lifting and carrying him into the lodge as Singing Bird warned, "Careful now, do not pull at him. His shoulders are hurt."

When Whirling Thunder emerged from the lodge he told what had happened. The young men, following the trail, had separated to fish and hunt. Little Eagle, found alone by four white men, had been set upon. Bee Hunter, Bear Cub and the others, hearing the commotion, had gone to his rescue. The white men grabbed their guns and ran for shelter at the sight of so many.

Black Hawk and Whirling Thunder slipped inside the lodge. Black Hawk moved toward the women working over Little Eagle. One motioned him away. Seeing this, Whirling Thunder went out to join his friends. As though drugged by the odor of steeping herbs heavy about him, Black Hawk stared at his son. The women had cleansed the bloody wounds and were preparing to apply their medicines.

Feeling useless, Black Hawk moved to where Swift Flying lay on the sleeping shelf. She was only half awake and restless. Gently he touched her face. Her skin was hot and dry against his hand.

He stared again toward the women and saw that Namequa stood near ready to hand them what they needed. Nasomsee, the ten-year old, must be telling other boys what had happened.

That night, so that Little Eagle might not be disturbed, all those in the lodge except Singing Bird and one of the aunts took their blankets to an empty lodge near by. The next morning when Black Hawk waited outside, Singing Bird, her face drawn and anxious, came out to him.

77

"He is no better. He cannot speak. The Evil Spirit of those white men has torn him inside. The Shaman must come."

Black Hawk hurried off, his heart pinched with fear. His lips moved silently, "Little Eagle, my son, my young warrior."

The Shaman came. Singing Bird and Black Hawk stood outside the lodge while he conducted his ceremonies within, alone. That night Singing Bird and Black Hawk crouched beside their first born, waiting.

"We have done what we could," whispered Singing Bird as they listened to the harsh, rasping gasps that filled the lodge.

Black Hawk stared into the flames so that he might not look on his child, nor see the pain in Singing Bird's eyes. For a long time there was no change. When the first gray light of the third day seeped through the cracks of the lodge, Black Hawk became aware that he heard only his own breathing. He reached out to touch his son. A great stillness possessed Little Eagle.

Singing Bird, crouched beside the boy, had covered her face. Her one braid, always so neatly wrapped, swung in straggling disarray as she rocked back and forth. Her thin wailing began and went on and on.

"My son is dead," said Black Hawk. "He has gone to the Great Spirit."

He pulled his blanket across his face and bent forward beside Singing Bird. Quickly the people gathered. Friends and relatives crowded into the lodge and they were no longer alone.

In her anxiety, Singing Bird had left Swift Flying in the care of others. Now, with Swift Flying demanding all her attention, she had scant time for mourning in the prescribed fashion.

She puzzled over what ailed the child and tried all her remedies. One night Swift Flying's throat filled up and she was unable to breathe. Then again the mourning sounds rose from Black Hawk's lodge.

When the old women had carried Swift Flying to the burying ground and she lay beside her brother, Black Hawk said, "Singing Bird, I shall mourn my children for two years. Then perhaps the Great Spirit will take pity on us."

Black Hawk and his family built a small lodge in their cornfield and gave away all their possessions so that they lived in poverty. Every day at sunset Singing Bird went to sit by the children's graves and, in ragged clothes and streaming hair, mourned for them. Black Hawk fasted, drinking a little water in mid-day, and eating only enough of the boiled corn at evening to keep him able to hunt and provide their scant living.

However much Black Hawk and his people resented the building of Fort Armstrong, it did bring them two friends, Colonel Davenport and Antoine LeClaire. In the spring of 1817, Colonel George Davenport built a double log house on Rock Island to serve as home and store.

In 1818 Antoine LeClaire came to Fort Armstrong as interpreter. LeClaire was the son of a Potawatomi mother and a French-Canadian father. In addition to English and French, he spoke numberless Indian tongues. Black Hawk had first talked with him in St. Louis and liked him though LeClaire, now twenty-one, was thirty years his junior.

Black Hawk visited the trading post often that summer of LeClaire's arrival. One day Davenport and LeClaire seated themselves on the floor with Black Hawk. Trade goods—piles of blankets, kettles, everything the Indians might want—crowded counters and shelves, even the one chair.

"Why does our agent keep saying I must leave the village?" asked Black Hawk.

"It was agreed in the treaty," said LeClaire.

"This treaty——" Black Hawk's hands spread in uncertain protest.

"Black Hawk——" Davenport started speaking in Sauk, then

turned to LeClaire. "You speak it better, Tony. Explain real good. I don't believe anyone has ever made it entirely clear to him."

LeClaire carefully went over the exact terms of the treaty, saying finally, "See, you'll have to leave Saukenuk, Black Hawk."

"But Quashquame says——"

"Oh, he sold it all right, way up to the Wisconsin River on this side. You yourself signed that next treaty at Portage des Sioux."

Black Hawk squirmed inside himself, too proud to admit he had not quite believed white men would take the village— other lands but not Saukenuk.

"It says we can stay here while the Great White Father owns it?"

"True enough. But soon the government will sell it," said LeClaire. "Isn't it better to go now and find yourself a good place across the Mississippi for a new village? The settlers will keep squatting on the land even if they don't own it."

"More every day—can't be stopped," agreed Davenport. "The settlers are liable to make it mighty uncomfortable for you."

Black Hawk's lips curled in a grim smile and he rubbed his smooth bare shoulder, still lame from a beating he himself had received.

"Many of our people have already felt their cruelty," he said and knew by their faces and their sympathetic looks that they had heard about Little Eagle.

"Wapello has agreed to go next spring," said LeClaire.

"You have great influence with him," said Black Hawk, nodding at Davenport who began unfolding his long legs. Rising, Davenport lifted his hand.

"Oh, Black Hawk—Keokuk has agreed to leave the village."

"Many will follow him," Black Hawk said aloud, and to himself, "but not all."

80

Black Hawk paddled toward the village with slow and sorrowful strokes as though he must take notice of this river that nourished his home. Once in mid-stream he put down the paddle, drew his blanket across his face and silently wept. For the first time he clearly understood that Saukenuk was lost. He might never again dip his paddle into the muddy, swift flowing Great River, so violent at times and again so sluggish and innocent of any evil intent, changeable as white men.

A few days later Keokuk sent a crier through the village, shouting his message. Elders and chiefs, Keokuk among them, moved to the council lodge.

"Our leader has spoken," said Neapope, with a sardonic twist of his lips.

"We shall see who will lead now," Black Hawk answered.

Speech making began. Keokuk talked for a long time, and finished saying:

". . . The war chief at Fort Armstrong and our trader Davenport tell us white men are many and it is best for us to leave. Let us go to the Ioway River. It is a good land. Join with me and we will build a fine new village. Then we will be troubled no more. I am done."

"Quashquame," said Crouching Eagle as old Tiamah nodded his agreement. "Tell us once more what you did. Be sure it is the truth."

Quashquame nervously fingered the shabby remains of finery the white men had given him and once more declared he had not sold Saukenuk.

Staring at him Black Hawk wondered. This man had always spoken the truth. Perhaps he did now. He may have understood as little as Black Hawk himself had understood until LeClaire had made it all too plain. Perhaps he himself had wanted to misunderstand thought Black Hawk in a moment of self revelation. Impatiently, he shrugged the thought away. Quashquame had acted without authority.

Old Tiamah lifted his finger.

"Black Hawk, what say you?"

Black Hawk rose and spoke slowly.

"Why must we wander off to the unknown regions of the West? We do not own that country. The deer, the elk, the buffalo, and the beaver, and the otter belong not to us and we have no right to kill them. It will only bring us to war with other tribes. Must we leave the bones of our ancestors resting here in Saukenuk to be desecrated by these white people?"

He lifted his fist and held it high above his head.

"I will not leave Saukenuk. Here our ancestors have lived for many moons and they knew their children's children would be born here and buried here. Saukenuk is my home . . . Here I will stay and those who wish may join me, defy the white men and stay in Saukenuk. I am done."

No unanimous decision could be reached. The council ended.

"We are about evenly divided, Black Hawk," said Neapope. "Perhaps you can bring Keokuk to our side."

Keokuk too felt the need of consultation. As he approached, Black Hawk noticed his rival's elegant otter head band and beaded leggings. His luxurious blanket and silver medal were doubtless the gifts of white friends in St. Louis.

Their talk accomplished nothing, save Keokuk's promise to visit Washington and give other land in exchange for Saukenuk. Word of this spread. There was hope among the people that Keokuk's smooth tongue would find a way to solve their difficulties.

Black Hawk's bitterness festered within him during these years as one season followed another and he watched the growing degradation of his people. Many depended on their government annuities, or made a poor hunt for lack of ammunition. With nothing to pay traders for supplies, they returned to shiftless living. Even young men were losing hope.

In a way mysterious to white people, news travelled surprisingly fast among the Indians. Thus, disturbing news reached Black Hawk one winter when they had gone northwest into the plains country of the Sioux in search of ever more scarce game.

At once he set out. Pushing hard he reached home in ten days, approaching Saukenuk in a roundabout way. Everywhere near his village well-trodden paths gave evidence of white settlers. Fences around their cornfields had been destroyed and replaced by others.

Caution cast aside, Black Hawk galloped down the trail. In the village some of the lodges had been torn down and stacked in piles as if for firewood.

He caught sight of his own lodge. There was a wagon, a great, clumsy thing, standing near it. Smoke was coming from the roof where a pipe had been put through the smoke hole. A heavily bearded man was chopping wood, apparently taken from a nearby lodge, and tossing it carelessly on a pile.

Black Hawk jumped from his horse and stood quietly until a woman appeared in the doorway. She wore an ugly dark dress under an all-enveloping apron and her gray hair was snaked back into a tight knot.

At her distressed cry, the man turned. With axe still in hand he stared warily at Black Hawk who saw that he was brawny, but fat across the stomach. The bushy growth of black whiskers waggled arrogantly with the rhythm of his jaws.

"Git out of here," he said, and spat out a brown stream of tobacco juice. Only his contemptuous manner meant anything to Black Hawk.

The man motioned toward the woman and she disappeared, then came running with a gun.

"Now git out of here," he said as he took it.

In spite of the gun, anger burning within him, Black Hawk stood his ground. Quietly, he made the gesture of peace by raising one hand. He told them he meant no harm, but they must leave his home. He made signs but they shook their heads.

"I will see Forsyth. I go to LeClaire," he said finally. "LeClaire," he repeated.

The man nodded then and pointed toward the Fort.

At the Fort Black Hawk found that Forsyth had gone to St. Louis for the winter. LeClaire greeted him and Black Hawk skipped the preliminaries of eating and smoking.

"There are white people in my village—living in my lodge," he said. "I do not want them there, harming my lodge. I do not want——"

LeClaire interrupted him.

"Easy, easy now, Black Hawk. Joshua Vandruff is the man. Many more are coming in he says."

"Write me a paper to give him," said Black Hawk. "They do not understand what I say."

"All right. What do you want me to tell them?"

LeClaire searched among the disorderly papers on his desk, found a clean sheet, then waited with quill poised.

"Tell him not to settle in our village. Tell him they must not harm our lodges or our fences. They must not settle in Saukenuk. He must leave my lodge. We are coming home in the spring."

Black Hawk waited as LeClaire's quill formed those queer, bird-like scratches. Then he took the paper and looked at it admiringly.

LeClaire followed him out and called, "Come back here for the night. Don't get mixed up with those white rascals."

Black Hawk grinned and waved acknowledgment. Then he folded the letter carefully and tucked it into his tobacco pouch.

At his lodge Black Hawk saw children dressed in their queer, smothering garments playing where his children had played. He stared at them until they scuttled inside, wailing some queer words. More swarmed into view, as many as the fingers of two hands, he noted with astonishment. When the man and his wife appeared, Black Hawk dismounted and handed the paper to Vandruff.

He read it aloud, haltingly, and said, "So you're Black Hawk. Well, I picked a good lodge to stay in, didn't I? We'll see who stays here in the spring. You can tell that breed LeClaire I got the letter."

Black Hawk took his smile for this man's good will. Wearily he returned to the Fort where he ate and spent the evening arguing with LeClaire and Davenport. At last the two men shook their heads and told him where he might spread his blanket for the night.

8. Betrayed by Friends

Before dawn Black Hawk stood outside the trading post chewing on the mixture of pounded, parched corn, meat, and maple sugar that Singing Bird had packed in the small deerskin bag he carried on his belt. No one was astir to see him start up river.

He crossed the Rock at the ford below the Prophet's Town, thirty-five miles above Saukenuk. As he guided his pony between the floating cakes of ice he mused that the holy man had chosen his location wisely. Prairie and bluff made a pleasing landscape. In summer, oak and locust lining the river bank gave a shady, protected place where the mixed group of Sauk and Winnebago following the Prophet had built their lodges.

Black Hawk was taken at once to White Cloud, the Prophet. Silently the holy man made a place beside him. He motioned toward the women and they brought food. After they had smoked Black Hawk said, "I have come to you for advice."

The Prophet pointed toward his wives, who faded from sight.

"You have communion with higher forces than I," said Black Hawk. The Prophet bent his head in agreement. His tangled black hair fell forward and his heavy eyelids drooped so that Black Hawk could read nothing in his eyes.

They sat together for a long time while Black Hawk talked. At last he said, "I grow tired of their saying we must cross the Mississippi."

Chin in hand, the Prophet spoke dreamily.

"Yet Quashquame insists that he did not give away Saukenuk."

"Is there any way——?"

The Prophet began scratching thoughtfully at his ribs. It occurred to Black Hawk that the Prophet would do well to bathe in the river, even in cold weather; and was annoyed that he should think of this during such serious talk.

"You are right, Black Hawk," said the Prophet. "The white people would only plow up the bones of your ancestors and scatter them."

"What must I do?"

"Remain in your village. The white people will not trouble you."

"But they have and how can I know——"

"This will cease. I feel it."

Troubled and doubtful, Black Hawk was silent. After a moment the Prophet went on.

"Urge Keokuk to bring all those home who have said they will go to the Ioway this spring. A show of force does much. Numbers can drive them away if you appear bold."

At the ponderous sureness of his tone, a cautious hope returned to Black Hawk. He straightened, reviving under the holy man's spell.

"Did you ever feel that you were the one to rally all the tribes against these evil white men?" asked the Prophet.

"Neapope has suggested it."

"You are a great leader. This may be the time—at last——"

The Prophet's watchful eyes were upon Black Hawk, drawing up his pride to smother wisdom and good judgment. Then slowly Black Hawk stopped reaching and slumped forward a little, drooping and aware of his inner self.

"Others have tried and failed. There is little chance that I could do better," he said abruptly.

"But with *my* help?" said the Prophet, his voice a soft purring in Black Hawk's ears. Then his tone became brisk. "Tell me, what chiefs can you depend on?"

"Neapope," he answered.

The Prophet's heavy face with the deep lines running from nose to chin changed as the sleepy eyes turned sharp and penetrating.

"The others?"

"Crouching Eagle, Atako and Pamaho. A few others—some cannot decide."

"What if you send the red wampum to many other tribes——"

Black Hawk stared into the fire and did not respond. Suddenly the Prophet said, "Ah, let us leave it there. I will commune with the Great Spirit."

In the morning Black Hawk began his long journey back to the hunting grounds, his mind toying with the ideas the Prophet had offered. He thought of Whirling Thunder, a handsome, capable young man in his prime, almost a foot taller now than Black Hawk, with shoulders as broad as his own. He too had dreamed of the Great God Thunder. He was a good talker—the right one to send if they decided to rally the tribes.

The moon had waxed and waned again while Black Hawk was gone from the hunting grounds. At the spring rendezvous for sugar making, Black Hawk and Keokuk exchanged sharp words. Keokuk had not yet visited Washington.

It was an unhappy homecoming that spring. Vandruff still occupied Black Hawk's lodge. The entire family, from bold-eyed young men and pretty girls to numerous small ones, poured out as Black Hawk stood before the lodge. His angry talk accomplished nothing but to bring on scornful laughter and a spate of obscenities.

Black Hawk rejoined his people huddled together waiting and stood for a moment in thought. Then Singing Bird saw a smile cross his face. He motioned her to him.

"Singing Bird, gather the relatives and their children. Bring all of them here. We will move into the lodge."

"But how can we?" she cried, her trembling hands worrying the little doeskin bag that held her beads and quills and bone sewing needles.

"It will be uncomfortable for awhile, but we will crowd them out, Singing Bird. White men say we do not smell good —they won't be able to stay with us."

Singing Bird burst into smothered laughter.

"They smell worse than we do—that dirty white man. I am sure neither he nor any of those children have been into the river once this spring."

Singing Bird hustled off, her shabby quill-decorated leggings fairly flapping in her haste to spread the joke.

Whirling Thunder brought his wife, children and all their many relatives. Namequa followed her mother, who appeared with other families. When all had gathered, Black Hawk led them into the lodge.

"Hey, you can't come in here," shouted Vandruff.

They paid no attention to the words they could not understand and crowded in. With a brushing motion, Black Hawk waved Vandruff to the far end of the lodge and, confronted with such a horde of people, the man did not pick up his gun.

Before the Vandruff family could decide what to do, all their possessions were shoved into one end of the lodge in a jumbled heap. The Indian women trotted in and out settling their household goods into place and, with much hilarity, investigating the cooking possibilities of the stove. Vandruff, muttering and fuming, headed for the Fort.

The Indian babies, without instructions from their elders, wandered toward the strange Vandruffs and lined up, solemnly fixing their black eyes upon everything the white people did until Mrs. Vandruff shooed them away. They darted off and like a flock of brown sparrows immediately drifted back again. The young men stared at the girls with knowing eyes until they shrank away behind their mother. Then the men stared at the mother until she waved her hands in helpless fury.

In a few days the Vandruffs moved. Black Hawk's guests departed, laughing as they went.

Vandruff established his family in a hastily erected cabin at the edge of the village. Here he operated his still and the place became the social center for brawling, drunken parties.

Many white men were selling whiskey to the Indians who bartered their guns, traps, horses—anything white men wanted. In the old days the elders might "take a frolic" when a trader gave them a little whiskey during a feast time. Then young men were busy fighting, hunting, and bragging over scalps taken. Now Black Hawk went from one white man to another saying, after LeClaire had taught him the words, "Stop sell my people whiskey," over and over, "Stop sell."

Year after year during the mid-twenties, Black Hawk visited the Indian agent, Thomas Forsyth, at Fort Armstrong to complain about the white people. Both Forsyth and Davenport were fully aware of how guilty the settlers were, destroying lodges, burning canoes, usurping cornfields, and abusing the Sauk on the slightest excuse. Sympathetic as they were, Forsyth and Davenport could do little but try to soothe Black Hawk.

Forsyth wrote to Clark, the Superintendent of Indian Affairs located in St. Louis, pleading the rights of the Indians. Reprimands to the settlers only brought counter complaints.

Demoralized by liquor, the Indians brought in fewer furs. Then, too, they were forced to go ever deeper into Sioux country for scarce game. Inevitably, fighting between tribes took time from hunting. Each fall Davenport forecast a poor hunt and fewer furs. Then once more, as their representative, he would receive complaints from John Jacob Astor's great American Fur Company.

During the mid-twenties too, white officials had been continually calling the chiefs of many tribes into council. The chiefs knew that would mean the white men wanted them to stop fighting among themselves, and another treaty signing away more of their lands. As a result of all this, common talk among the traders predicted a general uprising of the Indians that autumn of 1829.

When Black Hawk came as usual before he left for the hunting grounds to say goodbye to Forsyth, the agent told him the government would put the land up for sale in October. Davenport, in Washington, had sent him this news.

"Make it plain to him, LeClaire—when the sugar maples turn red and the willows are dried and yellow or something like that," said Forsyth, looking a bit startled at himself for putting it that way. "His right to remain here is at an end. He better get the straight of it this time."

Black Hawk had left before Davenport returned to Rock Island. Later that winter news that Davenport had bought Saukenuk filtered along the Indian grapevine. Black Hawk and the chiefs were infuriated.

In council, meeting without Keokuk's knowledge, it was decided that Davenport must be killed. Forsyth, LeClaire, the commandant at Fort Armstrong, and the agent Clark in St. Louis were also guilty. Keokuk was at fault too. He had not gone to Washington as he had promised. All these men must be killed.

On his return to Saukenuk that spring, Black Hawk went at once to the Fort. Forsyth, annoyed at his return, dismissed him when once more he refused to join the others on the Ioway River.

LeClaire walked with Black Hawk to the gate, urging him to take Forsyth's advice.

"I go to see Davenport," said Black Hawk.

LeClaire gave him a sharp look.

"I'd better go along. You may need me."

Davenport welcomed Black Hawk with a hearty handshake, brought pipes and tobacco, and they settled themselves to smoke and talk.

"I didn't expect to see you here," said Davenport.

"News reached us of what you did. I come to you now because you have betrayed us."

Davenport lifted a protesting hand.

"No, no. I have not betrayed you. My sons have played with your sons and with the sons of your people. I am your friend. I did what I could for your people."

"Then why did you buy our land?"

"It was to protect you that I bought it."

Black Hawk snorted in disgust, saying, "We had believed you were an honorable man."

"President Jackson, the Great White Father is a tough one." Davenport searched for the Sauk words. "Oh, Tony, you tell him—tell him I had to admit Black Hawk had fought against us. He banged his fist down on the table—'by the eternal,' he sez, 'every last one of them shall cross the Mississippi, or be killed.' "

LeClaire explained all this while Davenport leaned forward anxiously.

"What has that to do with your buying our lands?" asked Black Hawk.

"If I bought them I could let you stay—understand? You could live where you have always lived and trade with me. You see I benefit by that arrangement too. Doesn't that prove my good intentions?"

There was reason in it. If he could believe Davenport, then perhaps—— He lifted his eyes from contemplation of his pipe, then laid it aside, waiting.

"We could live happily together," Davenport went on.

"Do you think I could forget the many times your people have left bags of corn and squash and beans at my doorstep? Then why would I repay you by taking your land from you?"

"White men's ways are strange," said Black Hawk.

"When the Great Father insisted on selling the land, I had it surveyed. When it was put up for sale I bought your land, two thousand acres. A lot of country, Black Hawk. It would give you a place to hunt. Saukenuk would be safe."

"Then why do you insist that we must cross the river?"

LeClaire and Davenport exchanged uneasy glances.

"I could not get the President to let you stay. He would only postpone the time. 'Remember that,' he said, 'the first of April, 1830.'" Black Hawk stared at him, and Davenport wiped his sweating forehead with his shirtsleeved arm, adding, "You tell him, Tony. Make it plain."

Then, interrupting LeClaire, Davenport exclaimed, "What say to this, Black Hawk? If the Great White Father in Washington will take other lands in place of this, I will give this land back to the government. Even though the government won't do better for you than me, there's the offer. I will give this land back. Isn't that fair enough?"

"Colonel Davenport's word is as good as ours," said LeClaire. "You can believe him."

After further talk Black Hawk at last concluded that Davenport was honorable. Even though they both knew the Great Father would not allow this exchange of land, the offer was fair. It was a comfort, too, that Davenport promised he could be buried in the sacred land where his ancestors were buried.

Black Hawk returned to Saukenuk and called the plotters together. Slowly they were convinced, relieved perhaps, that they were not bound to do something that would only lead to more trouble. Neapope alone still frowned, but Black Hawk knew he would abide by their decision.

Not long after this Black Hawk, returning from the Fox

94

village one day, was nearing the cornfields when he heard a woman screaming. Topping a rise of ground on the run, he saw one of his own people—Namequa.

White men were yanking at her while she fought to free herself. Although strong and sturdy, Namequa was no match for two men.

Black Hawk yelled and ran. The men stared in his direction, still hanging onto her arms. Black Hawk had carried his gun, hoping for small game. The ammunition was gone, but he waved it menacingly. The men ran.

"They have hurt you," cried Black Hawk, seeing Namequa's torn clothing, her bruised face, and bleeding nose.

"I was working in the cornfield. They tried to drag me off."

Namequa was not pretty now, her face distorted with pain and fear. Heavy sobs shook her and tears mingled with the blood on her face.

Black Hawk led her home while Namequa tried to compose herself and wipe away the blood.

In their lodge Singing Bird tended to her bruises, and asked anxiously, "Did you have to go with them?"

"No. They were drunk or I could not have managed. Then my father heard me."

"It is not safe here now for our women," said Black Hawk to the relatives who had gathered.

Singing Bird cried out in distress.

"Must we go away? Can I never again sit beside Little Eagle's grave or my small one's to mourn them?" She laid a hand tenderly on Namequa's bruised cheek. "But how can we stay here if they do this to Namequa?"

She went on pouring out all the stories of abuse and mistreatment her neighbors had endured while the women around her nodded their heads.

"In the old days we were as happy as the buffalo on the plains," said an old wrinkled grandmother.

95

"Now we are as miserable as the hungry howling wolf on the prairie," said another.

Black Hawk looked at his daughter. She deserved better than this. She was a good woman. She had brought a good warrior and hunter into his lodge when she married. Now she and her two young children were without his protection, for he had been killed in battle with the Sioux. She scorned the young men who frittered away their time at Vandruff's.

He paced back and forth, thinking bitterly that the white people should have remained where the Great Spirit had placed them.

Soon he set out in search of advice. He visited Malden in Canada and the British piously assured him that if he had not sold his land, it could not be taken from him. In Detroit Lewis Cass, Governor of the Michigan Territory, agreed that this was true. Again Black Hawk talked with the Prophet.

In the autumn his mind was made up. He gathered a small group of warriors and supplied them with blue wampum, painted red for war. Led by Whirling Thunder, he sent them out to visit the Osage, the Cherokee, the Creek, and other tribes far to the south.

9. A Brave Showing

May, the moon of planting, had given way to the moon of flowering when word seeped up to Saukenuk that Governor Reynolds of Illinois had called for volunteers to assemble by the tenth of June; and that a great war chief was in St. Louis, planning to drive them out of their village.

Black Hawk sent off a runner to Prophet's Town and White Cloud, the Prophet, hurried down river. On his arrival they immediately fell to considering what should be done in the face of this and of the fact that Whirling Thunder's mission had ended in failure. No one had accepted the red war wampum.

Soon Keokuk and Wapello rode into Saukenuk, Keokuk looking more resplendent than ever. He reported that General Gaines was sailing up river, coming all this way to counsel with Black Hawk. At once Black Hawk consulted the Prophet.

After a night of communing with the Great Spirit, the Prophet advised Black Hawk, Neapope and all the chiefs to stay in Saukenuk and to refuse whatever the American war chief asked. That seemed a bit indefinite to Black Hawk, but he agreed and said, "We will make a brave showing when we are called into council. Then they will know we are determined and not afraid."

When, on Gaines' arrival, Black Hawk received the summons to the council, he and his warriors, fully armed, painted, and with red roaches tossing on their heads, gave their spine-tingling war whoops as they approached the council lodge.

They milled around outside until LeClaire came to investigate. Black Hawk refused to enter until Keokuk's warriors had left the room; only Keokuk and Wapello were to remain. Then, LeClaire beside him, General Gaines opened the council.

"I have called you here to remind you of your promises. Your chiefs have signed treaties three times—in 1804, 1816 and 1825. In these treaties you made a promise . . . You have been permitted to stay here as we agreed. Now many white people have come among you and you must keep your promise. What have you to say to this?"

For the hundredth time Quashquame in his whining voice told of his part in the treaty of 1804. Listening, Black Hawk thought it small wonder the white people were tired of hearing him. The old man finished and the white chief read from the paper LeClaire said was the treaty of 1804.

Black Hawk rose to speak, knowing that he too repeated words he had spoken many times.

On hearing LeClaire's translation, Gaines' face turned a deep purple. He rose and cried angrily, "Who is this Black Hawk that he has the right to speak for his tribe? He is not your leader."

Black Hawk stepped back, jarred by the harsh tone.

Controlling his anger during the moments of LeClaire's translation, Gaines went on sternly.

"The President is very sorry to be put to the trouble and expense of sending a large body of soldiers here to remove you from lands you have long since ceded to the United States . . . Your Great Father asks nothing but what is reasonable and right. I hope you will consult your best interest and go to the other side of the Mississippi."

The speeches went on at length. Finally General Gaines muttered to LeClaire, then rose and said, "I have come here neither to beg nor hire you to leave your village . . . My business is to remove you, peaceably if I can, but forcibly if I must. Tomorrow decide—but know this. If you do not cross the Mississippi, I will adopt measures to force you."

LeClaire had hardly finished when Gaines rose to leave the council lodge. Black Hawk blocked the way and held out his hand.

"You have asked who I am. I am Black Hawk, a Sauk. My father was a great war chief, so was his father before him. I am a great warrior and my people have followed me in many wars. Then know this. Black Hawk is satisfied with the lands the Great Spirit has given him. Why then should he leave them?"

After listening to LeClaire's translation, Gaines replied, "White men love their lands too, but, when they sell them, they leave. That is my answer."

He made a dismissing gesture and stalked from the room, followed by his aides.

Days slipped by. Putting his faith in Keokuk and considering him the real leader of the Sauk tribe, Gaines delayed action. To rid himself of one he thought a trouble maker, he sent the Prophet back to his own village. As further inducement, and on Keokuk's advice, he promised corn to those who would leave within three days.

While Black Hawk hesitated, Neapope volunteered to go to the British in Malden for help. Meanwhile Black Hawk gave orders for the people to stay quietly in their lodges. No guns were to be fired.

"Let them kill us if they will," he said in desperation, hoping that British help might come in time.

At twilight Nasomsee rode into the square raising a cloud of dust. He leaped from his horse and it stood all in a lather with sides heaving and head lowered.

"My Father," he shouted. "Many men on horseback are coming this way."

"Are they those they call the militia?"

"They are not regular soldiers."

Keokuk had warned him of this repeatedly. Black Hawk sent out five of his warriors to spy, then drew his son aside to question him before hurrying to the council lodge. Soon the spies brought word that the militia had camped for the night.

As though the gods were speaking, wind moaned in the trees and the smell of blown dust came to their nostrils. The chiefs turned to Black Hawk expectantly.

"These militia cannot be trusted to act like warriors," said Black Hawk. "Our women and children are not safe."

"Their officers have no control over them," said Crouching Eagle.

Black Hawk's order came sharp and quick.

"We must take our people away—across the Mississippi. That is the only safe place now."

A few drops of rain pattered on the roof. Distant thunder rumbled.

"A storm coming," said Crouching Eagle.

"We must start at once," said Black Hawk. "We will go to every lodge ourselves. Rouse the people. Let them take what they can bundle up quickly and get to the canoes."

He stepped to the door and called, "Bee Hunter, Bear Cub."

They answered and came from the shadows to take orders.

"Gather the young men. Get to the other side with the horses. Take them one by one, so that any watcher will think only a lone person crosses. Take them to the point and cross as far down from the Fort as you can—but choose different places. Cross the Rock and then the Great River if it seems best that way—but hurry."

"It is done," said Bee Hunter.

Whirling Thunder ran up.

"Join Bee Hunter," said Black Hawk. "I have given him the orders. Some of you must wait until after the women have started. You, Whirling Thunder, leave me one horse. We will meet on the far side."

Under cover of darkness, the young men slipped away into the meadows where the horses grazed or slept. If the warriors disturbed them, any unusual noise was lost in the sound of wind wailing through the trees.

Up and down the rows of lodges went the chiefs. The women woke, roused the children, and kept all quiet. Through the village people moved swiftly, yet there was little sound and no light. If a startled child wailed it was but momentary.

One by one the canoes put out into the river, following closely along the south side of the channel where the trees overhung the bank, then out into the more turbulent current of the Mississippi.

Black Hawk roused his own household. All worked swiftly. Gathering a few necessities they hastened to the river.

Singing Bird and Namequa lashed two canoes together and with Namequa's two small children and the Old Ones of their lodge climbed in. All around them other women were setting out.

"I am strong, Father," said Namequa. "So is my mother."

"Hush, my child. Do what you can. I will find you on the other side." He turned to his wife. "Singing Bird——" Her murmured answer came, "Black Hawk."

His favorite horse nudged at his shoulder. He heard Whirling Thunder's voice saying, "All the horses are gone, Father," before he rode off into the darkness.

Black Hawk pushed the canoes away from shore. When the lightning flashed he saw them moving out into mid-stream. He lifted his hands and silently called on the Great Spirit to protect them and all his people. Once more he rode up and down the streets calling softly until he was sure no one had been left behind.

Now he was free to go. Beside his horse Black Hawk

plunged into the Rock River, crossed, and made his way in the darkness to the Mississippi. By doing this he avoided the more difficult crossing where Rock and Mississippi joined.

For a moment he looked back toward the Fort. Even in daylight it might not have been visible from where he stood, and through the wind-blown violence of the whipping rain he could see nothing. Surely no one there would realize what they were doing.

The rain beat down upon him fiercely as he struck out into the depths. He felt the current take hold. The water pitched and boiled, throwing him against the side of his horse, testing his utmost strength.

Lightning flashed again and again. Thunder rolled along the river. Rain blinded him. Still Black Hawk struggled on knowing that he and his horse were being carried far down river. At length, he could only cling to the animal's mane.

When he stumbled out onto the other shore he lay exhausted, his eyes closed. Without his strong, young horse Black Hawk knew he could never have made the crossing. He reached up and fondled the head drooping beside him. The velvet nostrils quivered in response.

He thought of Singing Bird, Namequa, her children, and the Old Ones. Surely they must be safe—somewhere he would find them.

In a moment he would get up and start gathering the people together. The night was far spent and the rain had stopped. His horse snorted a little and sighed heavily. Black Hawk rose and in the dim light saw one of his men approaching.

"Bee Hunter?" he called. "Ride south and bring back any who have gone farther down. I will go up river and find a place for us to gather."

"You are tired," said Bee Hunter. He came and clasped his hands so that Black Hawk could mount more easily, turning his face away that he might not see it done.

"This night has made an old man of me, my son," said Black Hawk, managing a chuckle at his own weakness.

"Sometimes old men have great wisdom," said Bee Hunter, waiting so that Black Hawk might not see how easily he leaped upon his own horse.

At last all the people were gathered together. In silence, staring up river toward Saukenuk, the bedraggled group heard the gunfire and saw the sky begin to glow a faint red.

"It is not the morning sun," said Crouching Eagle.

The huddled women stirred and murmured. The men gathered in knots and pointed. Black Hawk was silent, knowing what it was. Cold, wet, and hungry they waited and at Black Hawk's order raised a white flag.

Whirling Thunder, Nasomsee, and Bear Cub had not appeared. Bee Hunter was sure they had stayed behind or gone back to spy. The chiefs waited anxiously until the young men rejoined their people.

"They acted like madmen when they found we were gone," said Nasomsee angrily. "I got close. We watched them throw a body into the fire. It was a small one—at first we feared one of the children had been left behind. Then we knew——"

"They have desecrated our burying grounds," said Whirling Thunder with bitter hatred.

An angry murmur rose around them. Somewhere in the crowd the wailing of a woman began, then another and another.

Before the chiefs could make any decision, a canoe was sighted. Keokuk pulled in to shore. He had left his finery behind and his manner was worried and anxious.

"The great war chief summons you to a council, Black Hawk," he said. "All the chiefs. You must come, Black Hawk. I am fearful for our people. The war chief is very angry. He tells me if you do not return he will attack you."

In the silence that had fallen upon them, he drew Black Hawk aside and for once spoke humbly.

"I beg you to come with me, Black Hawk. I beg you. I do not wish to see you punished in this way. I am not heartless, even if you think me so."

Black Hawk was silent while the others waited. Finally he said, "We see things in a different way, Keokuk."

"You know what happened to the village?" asked Keokuk. "They are ruthless. But the war chief Gaines—he will treat you well if you will come and sign the treaty. Come, I beg you."

"Very well, Keokuk. I will return. There is little else I can do now."

Keokuk sighed with relief and there was neither triumph nor arrogance about him.

"Prepare yourselves," Black Hawk said to the chiefs. "We will go with Keokuk at once."

The chiefs hurried to their families to give them instructions and comfort. Black Hawk went to see that all was well with those of his lodge. He found Singing Bird huddled on the ground, bent over.

"Why do you weep so, Singing Bird?"

"It might have been our little one they threw on the fire."

"Or some other," he said gently.

"And the squash vines. I had planted the seeds this spring so carefully. They had made such a good start. I weep for these things, my husband—and for much more."

"Yes, much more. Weep, Singing Bird. If you will."

He talked of what must be done, then he left them.

From well up river they could still hear the wailing of the women. Black Hawk could not bring himself to look back.

Black Hawk, knowing himself a bedraggled figure, stood before General Gaines and summoned up all his dignity and pride to clothe his shame.

"Articles of Agreement and Capitulation" read Gaines . . . "that you have come to sue for peace . . . these conditions: . . . never again cross the Mississippi without the express permission of the President of the United States, and of the Governor of the State of Illinois . . . abandon all communication and cease to hold any intercourse with any British post, garrison or town . . . and that you submit to Keokuk's authority . . ."

Black Hawk's ears heard the words the interpreter translated and he saw that LeClaire could not look at him but kept his eyes fixed on the paper in his hand. This son of a Potawatomi woman knew no greater shame could be put upon Black Hawk—that he, a great war chief, must bow to the authority of such as Keokuk, a lesser chief considered powerful only by white men.

LeClaire began to read the names. One by one each chief stepped forward. LeClaire read Black Hawk's name and held out the goose quill, his forefinger pointing to the place where Black Hawk must make his mark.

Silence beat upon Black Hawk's head. Slowly he took the quill and, with the bold and violent stroke of unwilling acceptance, made his mark. Courteously he handed the blunted quill back to LeClaire.

It was done. This was the end of his rebellion. He would struggle no longer. Physically and emotionally exhausted, Black Hawk believed he had given up the fight.

When he returned to the camp, elders and lesser chiefs stood silently before him.

"I have touched the goose quill to their paper," he said. "Tell the people—we will go up the Ioway, beyond Keokuk's village, and that of Wapello——" For an instant he was unable to say it, then spoke firmly. "There we must make our village."

10. The Decision

The people settled into their makeshift, poverty-striken village on the Ioway River. Warriors and young boys tried to return to Saukenuk to bury the wantonly exhumed corpses; and again to harvest their crops. Both times they were fired upon and driven off.

One day Singing Bird, gossiping by the river with friends while she worked on a basket, glanced up and saw a canoe approaching. Shading her eyes against the light, she stared at the single occupant. Then hastily gathering up basket and reeds she ran toward the lodge to tell Black Hawk that Neapope had returned.

After Black Hawk and the young chief had smoked, Neapope explained the difficulties of his travels and his failure to bring help from the British right then—but the British had not deserted them.

"Be assured of that," said Neapope. "I stopped to see the Prophet. The holy man has received promises from the British."

"They travelled faster than you," said Black Hawk.

There was some censure in his voice but Neapope ignored it.

"In the spring British ships will send supplies to us by way of Milwaukie."

A sigh came from the depths of Black Hawk's being.

"A-ah. I have felt sure we could depend on our British Father."

"There is more." Neapope looked directly at Black Hawk for the first time. "The Prophet has received wampum from Ottawa, Chippewa and Potawatomi. The Winnebago will do anything he says."

At this, Black Hawk felt the vigor of youth pulse within him.

"Our people will follow you as no one else, Black Hawk."

Black Hawk closed his eyes and was silent, remembering youthful glories. Then he spoke thoughtfully. "There can be no happiness if we are prevented from returning to Saukenuk when the sap rises in the maple trees. I could—try—once more."

"Good. I urge you—talk again with the Prophet," said Neapope. "He has great power."

Black Hawk snapped a finger at his ear bob, deep in thought until Neapope's words startled him to attention.

". . . and if we should be whipped, there's a place north on the Red River where——"

Black Hawk stiffened.

"I do not lead my warriors into a losing battle."

Hastily Neapope agreed and Black Hawk spoke cautiously. "I do begin to hope that one day the sky may be clear for us."

He sat quietly after Neapope had left, sifting sand between his fingers. It had seemed so easy when Neapope struck the first spark of hope. He could rally the chiefs. Why did his mark on a piece of paper mean so much?

He wandered to the river and walked there alone. Troubled by the dangers ahead if he undertook this thing, in anguish over the fate of his people, Black Hawk at last found himself far up river.

Must he submit as Keokuk had done—maneuver and plot while seeming in the eyes of white people to do what was best for his tribe and thus gain advantage for himself? No. He had already gone too far on another course to play that game, had he any wish to do so. If he did not revenge the people's injuries, they would think him a woman, or too weak to be a chief.

He raised his hands high and called on the Great Spirit.

"Give me a sign, Great Spirit, give me a sign."

The British had told him many times that they would help him. He had no reason then to doubt Neapope and the Prophet.

"Great Spirit, speak."

Far away like a wild animal disturbed, the God of Thunder growled. A hawk sailed into view on an updraft, silhouetted against a patch of sky where mare's tails clouds feathered the blue.

"The sign is given," he whispered in awe, and thanked the Great Spirit.

In the morning Neapope came to him again and Black Hawk said, "Tell the Prophet we will be ready in the spring."

He sent Whirling Thunder to Keokuk who came running to protest, saying that the Prophet and Neapope could not be trusted. Black Hawk hesitated before his earnestness, but finally said, "If nothing good comes from Washington in the spring——" and made a violent downward stroke with his fist.

Through the winter Black Hawk travelled among the Kickapoo, Potawatomi, Winnebago, and Fox villages. Many bands promised to join him. In late winter he called Neapope, Whirling Thunder, and Bear Cub to him and proposed a plan.

"Say nothing of this to anyone. If it works, our women and children and the Old Ones will have a place of safety in our village. If not—we must find another."

On a bright, crisp day the march from Black Hawk's village on the Ioway began. Women, children, and the old people set out by canoe. The warriors mounted their horses and, with a beating of drums, followed Black Hawk toward Keokuk's village.

Keokuk received them graciously. Black Hawk ordered the war post set up and soon the frenzy of the war dance mounted higher and higher. When it lessened momentarily, Black Hawk sprang forward and shouted them to silence.

He began reciting all the grievances of their people, saying at last: " . . . will you, the descendants of our great and illustrious dead stand idly by? Have you lost your strength and courage and become women? The Great Spirit whispers no! Let us cross the Mississippi . . . sound forth the war whoop of the united Sauk and our cousins the Fox, Potawatomi, Ottawa, Chippewa, Winnebago will join us . . . The British Father will send guns, ammunition, and soldiers. Then will the deadly arrow and fatal tomahawk hurtle through the air at the hearts and heads of paleface invaders."

The crowd roared. One after another Keokuk's warriors rushed forward to sink their tomahawks deep in the war post.

Black Hawk cried out, "Speak Keokuk, join with us."

It was evident that most of his warriors were ready to desert Keokuk—they might even kill him if he refused to lead them. Again Black Hawk flung up his hand, "Speak Keokuk, what has the leader of the Peace Band to say now?"

Keokuk moved forward, but did not touch the war post. Silence fell on the people.

"I have heard your demand to be led forth upon the war path against the palefaces. Their cabins are as many as the trees in the forest. Their soldiers are springing up like grass on the prairies. All we can reasonably expect is to wreak the utmost of our vengeance on their hated heads and fall, when fall we must, our faces to the enemy."

His melodious, hypnotic voice commanded them.

"It is my duty as your chief to be your father while in the

112

paths of peace, your leader while on the war path. You have decided to follow the path of war, and I will lead you to victory if the Good Spirit prevails——"

Now his voice struck down the rising clamor.

"But what shall we do with our old and infirm, our women and children? We dare not leave them behind us . . ."

The women drew small children close against them as Keokuk recited their fate in lurid detail. The Old Ones shrunk within their blankets as Keokuk's voice in rich and powerful cadence painted a vivid picture.

". . . I will lead you on one condition—that first we put our wives and children, our aged and infirm, gently to sleep in the slumber that knows no waking this side of the spirit land——" A gasp rose from every throat in the stunned crowd and his voice sharpened . . . "In a few short moons we follow them, but they must not follow us. This sacrifice is demanded of us by the very love we bear these dear ones. We cannot take them with us, we dare not leave them behind."

In the paralyzed silence that Keokuk permitted to lengthen a low murmur rose among the women. Keokuk turned to Black Hawk.

"I appeal to you, venerable chief. Your long experience upon the war path tells you I have spoken the truth, yet, with all your wonderful eloquence, you have urged us to this terrible sacrifice . . . By flattery and hypocrisy evil counsellors who speak with forked tongues have gained your confidence . . . They told you the British Father has promised assistance. Where are their arms and equipment?"

Black Hawk saw the crowd shift uneasily.

"The British Father neither knows nor cares . . . Your evil counsellors have told you that the moment you sound your war whoop east of the Mississippi all the tribes between that and the Illinois River will unite with you. Why are they not here now? . . . I beseech you, abandon this desperate under-

113

taking . . . if you still persist then indeed may we bid farewell to Black Hawk whose protecting spirit has forsaken him . . .''

Keokuk's oratory had done its damage. With fierce cries warriors rushed forward and wrenched their tomahawks from the war post. Black Hawk and Neapope moved swiftly among their own men to hold all possible to their purpose.

That night, sheltered in the wickiup Namequa and Singing Bird had hastily constructed by tying saplings together at the top and covering them with mats, Black Hawk slept fitfully. The first cheeping of birds began. Leaving the sleepers, he went outside. Neapope came to squat beside him.

Black Hawk was determined there should be no change in plans. They would start down river, delaying only to rally and encourage their own warriors.

"Mid-day will be time enough then?" asked Neapope.

Black Hawk nodded, saying, "All those who go by canoe will start down river as we planned. Mounted warriors will follow me to meet those who have gathered where the old Fort Madison stood. Atako and Pamaho should be moving north with them now. When we join forces we will cross the ford at Oquawka. From there we will travel together up the Great River."

Daylight had come. The camp was astir, the still air pungent with the smoke of first fires, cooking pots steamily simmering. Dogs were sniffing at cast-off bones, the children running about to explore unfamiliar surroundings.

When the sun was directly overhead and the canoes on their way, Black Hawk led his warriors from camp. After meeting the Potawatomi, Kickapoo, Chippewa and Winnebago at the rendezvous they moved on together, principal chiefs in the lead.

Black Hawk touched his horse and it pranced sideways so that he could look back. It was an impressive and glorious sight—nearly two thousand people on the move.

His warriors were in battle dress, long tufts of red-dyed

horsehair tied at their elbows; lances held high, aflutter with pennants, feathers and scalp locks; every Sauk's handsome red roach ruffled and tossing in the breeze; turkey and eagle feather ornaments, otter fur head bands, leggings and war aprons heavily quilled or beaded.

Later they would paint with white clay and make the black hand prints on their bodies, placing the circlets of straw or leaves on head and ankles. Then the white men would tremble and know that they were meeting Black Hawk's mighty warriors.

In the line of canoes Black Hawk saw those of his own lodge, and was thankful for Namequa's strength. Still, he would be glad if his plan for the women's safety could be carried out.

"Look who comes," cried Neapope.

Nasomsee and Bear Cub, returning from a scouting foray, rode with another horseman.

"Ah, White Cloud, the Prophet," said Black Hawk.

Prancing horses drew up before them, and the younger men fell back respectfully.

"You bring news?" asked Black Hawk.

"I am an emissary from Fort Armstrong," said the Prophet, assuming a look of extreme piety. "They requested me to turn you back."

Neapope stared at him in shocked disbelief.

"Who would have thought it of you," said Black Hawk with a wry twist of his mobile lips.

Neapope glanced from one to the other. The two older men smiled. The Prophet then reported that, speaking with the smoothness of a Keokuk, he had told the white men that he had invited them to make corn with him. Reminded of the Agreement not to cross the Mississippi, he had pretended he thought that only meant they must stay away from Saukenuk, but could go farther up the Rock River.

"Only the Great Spirit knows how I hate white men," he muttered.

"Is that all?" asked Black Hawk, seeing the Prophet's face turn sullen and not wanting him to lapse into one of his brooding silences.

"Atkinson, the White Beaver, is on the way up to Rocky Island."

Black Hawk rubbed a finger thoughtfully along his ear bob.

"If we go peaceably the white men cannot harm us," said the Prophet.

"They know we do not take all our people with us when we go to war," said Neapope. "That should convince them we go in peace."

Some slight plucking of apprehension, a moment of foreboding lived in Black Hawk—but it passed.

"Does this change our plan for the Fort?" asked Neapope.

"No, that stands," said Black Hawk. "One powerful stroke now and we will be too much for the White Beaver."

By mid-afternoon of the seventh day they were approaching the place where the Rock River flowed into the great Mississippi. At Black Hawk's order drumming and chanting began. Women's voices joined in from the river. Now white men would know they were not afraid, thought Black Hawk.

The horses pricked up their ears and set up a delicate prancing and tossing of manes. All along the line the barking of dogs increased the bedlam. Black Hawk smiled. The white people must be shivering in their lonely cabins as the terrible Indians passed.

In the late afternoon they made camp at Mill Creek on the south side of the Rock River, across from the ashes of Saukenuk. The men began painting for war and readying weapons. The women stared across the river in silence. Bear Cub and Whirling Thunder had special orders. Selecting a canoe, they hid it in readiness under the low-hanging willows.

Bear Cub, strong yet slight of build, had a reputation for moving quietly and silently. Whirling Thunder had great strength. Some of the warriors were to stay behind to protect their dependents.

A little before sunset Black Hawk led two hundred warriors out from camp. They forded the Rock River and crossed the peninsula, heading toward Rock Island. In full view of Fort Armstrong, they came to a halt.

"They are watching us," said Neapope.

"It is better that they look here," said Black Hawk, glancing proudly over his well-disciplined force.

Suddenly a soft grayness filled the air, dimming the last of the sunset. A little wind sprang up and lifted the feathers tied in the manes of the horses. Neapope nodded toward the west. Black Hawk made a quick decision.

"I shall go myself to the caves. I know them better than anyone."

Neapope frowned and spoke anxiously.

"Your orders?"

"As soon as it is dark enough so you cannot be seen lead them across. Hide in the woods. I will rejoin you, but do not wait for me. Attack, as we planned, as soon as you hear it."

Black Hawk called the chiefs, telling them Neapope was in command. In the gathering dusk he rode swiftly away. Near the place where the canoe waited, he gave the night hawk's cry, and heard the answer. Leaving the horse in a copse near-by, he went to the river.

"Neapope," a voice whispered, then a hiss of suspicion before he dropped into the canoe.

"I have come myself," he said. "I must be sure of this."

He sensed a feeling of relief in the young men as Bear Cub exclaimed softly, "Snow."

"Yes, I felt it on my face," said Whirling Thunder.

"It is time," said Black Hawk. "Now."

They shoved the canoe out into the river and moved quietly upstream. Close to the rock, feeling their way, Whirling Thunder whispered, "This is the place."

Bear Cub held the canoe beside the opening. Black Hawk climbed into the cave first and received the three kegs that Whirling Thunder heaved up to him. Bear Cub leaped up and they rolled the kegs deeper into the cave. Bear Cub began scattering the trail of powder.

Whirling Thunder's voice came to them in a piercing whisper.

"There is a boat coming. Hurry."

"Make it thick," urged Black Hawk.

They neared the entrance. Whirling Thunder held the canoe ready, muttering, "Hurry, hurry."

Great soft flakes of snow were drifting down more thickly now, muffling all sounds.

Bear Cub tried to strike fire, but failed. Black Hawk seized flint and steel from him and they moved farther back into the cave.

"It burns," whispered Bear Cub as they both crouched protectingly over the flame.

For a moment the men were motionless, eyes on the feebly flickering sputter of the gun powder. In that instant they heard the booming of a big gun.

"White Beaver," exclaimed Black Hawk. "Get out."

They plunged toward the entrance, dropped into the canoe and thrust it away, paddling frantically, close to the shelving rock. Then they were free and pulling toward the east end of the island.

There Black Hawk brought them safely to a landing place.

"It should have exploded by now," said Black Hawk.

"It was burning," said Bear Cub. "We paddled swiftly. Has there been time?"

"Time enough. We have failed," said Black Hawk.

"If the Good Spirit had only been there to shield it with his big white wings," said Whirling Thunder bitterly.

"The Good Spirit was driven out when the white men came," said Black Hawk.

They leaped onto the slippery bank, and Bear Cub was left to make his way back, get Black Hawk's horse and, if need be, help protect their people in the encampment.

Again the cry of the night hawk signalled. When they reached the warriors, Black Hawk found one of the scouts had seen the boat and had given warning. Neapope had held the warriors back, uncertain what he should do when the cannon boomed.

Admitting failure, Black Hawk gave his orders. In the morning only the droppings from their horses were left to tell the white men that Indians had menaced them in the night.

At daylight the Indians were on the march again, drumming and singing. Twice Sauk messengers came to them from White Beaver, the first saying: "It is not too late to do what is right, and what is right do at once." The second threatened that the White Beaver's troops would sweep over them like the fire over the prairie.

Black Hawk snorted in disgust.

"Tell him that he will find the grass green and not easily burned. If he wishes to fight us, let him come on."

He spat contemptuously and turned to Neapope.

"I could plant and raise corn and keep out of the way of White Beaver, but I will not be driven and I will not make an attack until all our forces are gathered. Let him come if he will."

Later Henry Gratiot, agent to the Winnebago, bringing with him chiefs from Turtle Village, came under a white flag. He too urged Black Hawk to go back across the Mississippi.

The Winnebago chiefs, White Crow and Man Eater, managed, under cover of scowls and threatening looks but with words strange to Gratiot, to convey their sympathy and encouragement. If they would not fight with Black Hawk, they would at least give aid.

"He wants to take your answer to White Beaver," said Broken Shoulder.

"Tell him my heart is bad, that I will not go back. I intend to go on up the Rock River. I will fight any force the white men send against me."

11. A Flag of Truce Unhonored

Later Black Hawk sat in council with the Winnebago chiefs and elders from other villages. There was none of the enthusiasm for the cause that Neapope and the Prophet had led him to expect. The Winnebago chiefs had no intention of joining him, nor did they want him to go up river.

"The White Beaver will not let me stay here," said Black Hawk. "You do not want us to go up river." He gave a harsh laugh. "Tomorrow we will start for Kishwaucokee River. There is nothing else we can do." He looked from one to the other. "Surely that is plain to you?"

They had no answer. Neapope and the Prophet followed Black Hawk from the council. When they were beyond the hearing of the Winnebago, Black Hawk spoke.

"Neapope, what of this?"

"Can I help it if they accept the wampum and then turn cowards?"

"You should have been sure," said Black Hawk, his voice sharp edged. Angry and feeling himself betrayed by this younger friend he had trusted, Black Hawk turned to the Prophet.

"And you, many times you told me I could expect help here. You both said you had promises from the British."

"Now, now," said the Prophet soothingly, and began his meditative scratching. "Here you have found few bold young warriors, but farther up river other villages of the Winnebago will join us."

"Those who came with Gratiot seemed to think I could expect little real help," said Black Hawk.

Their silence was answer enough. Finally the Prophet spoke.

"If my hatred of the white man leads you to failure, the gods have lied to me."

His eyes closing to slits, he lost himself in that hatred.

"Once they see this glorious show of all our warriors they will join us," said Neapope with his customary arrogance.

"No word has come from the British. What of that, Neapope?"

Neapope glanced uneasily at the Prophet.

"It will come. It will come," said the Prophet.

"When we camp for the night above your town," said Black Hawk to the Prophet, "I will talk with the chiefs."

He left them and went to lie by Singing Bird. As he pulled the blanket about him, he found her still wakeful.

"All goes well?" she whispered anxiously.

"Not well," he answered, and because it must be said, "Neapope has been deceiving me. Tomorrow we must push on."

"I am afraid, Black Hawk. Ever since they burned Saukenuk I have been afraid."

Under the blanket he put his arm around Singing Bird, held her close, and found that she trembled.

"Do not be afraid, my sweet Singing Bird. I will not let them harm you."

"The white men are so cruel—all the women are afraid. And the children—when they are old enough to understand. But it is for you I am afraid."

"Enough, Singing Bird, let us not speak more of it lest our courage fail us."

At dawn, only a scattering of young, untried Winnebago

warriors came to join Black Hawk. That night they camped well above the Prophet's Town and, when the people had settled into quiet, Black Hawk and the chiefs gathered.

In the council Black Hawk told them that Neapope had deceived him. They could expect little from the Winnebago. Amidst angry murmuring the Prophet protested that he too had been deceived. The chiefs decided the people must not be told or they would lose courage. The Prophet, as usual, was ready with advice.

"Tell them that the British Father will send help in a few days," he said.

Black Hawk agreed, remembering how many times the British had helped him and so hoped that upon this, at least, he might depend. He looked toward Neapope, and said, "Or will this too prove false?"

For once Neapope's manner was subdued and uncertain.

Before they began moving next morning, Keokuk and Wapello rode into camp and urged them to return. Keokuk's intervention only strengthened Black Hawk's determination.

"*You* will do nothing. I must take this chance for our people."

"It is death. The Long Knives are many——"

"Yes, yes. I know—as the trees in the forest and the leaves on the trees."

Black Hawk raised his arm. Keokuk and Wapello drew aside and watched the line move out up river.

Black Hawk's people made camp at Kishwaucokee. There were many Potawatomi villages in this area and Black Hawk had hoped to be welcomed. No one appeared so he sent messengers asking them to counsel with him.

By late afternoon a group of Potawatomi arrived. At once warriors and chiefs crowded close. It had not gone unnoticed among the people that few recruits were joining them. Even the women hovered anxiously on the outskirts, hoping to overhear what was said.

When Black Hawk and the chiefs drew them away from the people, the Potawatomi men declared they had no corn or supplies of any kind that could be spared. They protested they were a peaceful people and had never promised Neapope that they would join Black Hawk.

"Have you received any news from the British?"

"What should we hear?" they exclaimed.

"That a chief of our British Father was coming to Milwaukie with ammunition and guns for us."

While they stared at him in astonishment, Black Hawk's last hope drained away.

"Wild tales," exclaimed one of the younger men. "We know nothing of this. Someone has lied to you."

"Ah yes," said Black Hawk sadly. "I'm afraid someone has."

Black Hawk escorted his guests to their sleeping place and, before returning to Singing Bird, walked a little by himself.

Before he had fought one battle he was tasting the bitterness of defeat. It was humiliating to start out so bravely and come to this—fizzle out, as the gun powder had fizzled in the cave. Daily his spies were bringing him word of armies gathering close behind him at Dixon's Ferry. Soon White Beaver might order pursuit.

Provisions were growing short. Game had been driven from prairie and forest. There was little to add to their small supply of corn and beans. Had Neapope imagined the gods would multiply this or had he only been careless?

And the British? Was that too a product of Neapope's imagination? Was there anything left for him to do but raise the white flag and confess defeat?

In the morning he sent for Neapope and the Prophet.

"I have been caught in a net of lies," said Black Hawk. "Neapope, what did you want to do? Make a fool of me? Betray your people? I have led them into great danger because of your promises."

126

"I am no more to blame than the Prophet," said Neapope. "He promised help from the Winnebago and Potawatomi."

"He took your word about the British—and enlarged on it, perhaps. You are even."

"The British agent might have spoken without authority," said Neapope, embroidering on his lie. "But you—you have always been successful in war."

The talk of a child, thought Black Hawk.

"I am not a god," he said grimly. "Perhaps for a time I dreamed I was, but I cannot do this alone—that is certain."

He paced restlessly. Had the gods deceived the Prophet? How strange. The gods too must have been deceived. No, that was impossible. Now in Black Hawk's estimation, the holy man was diminished.

"I have decided," said Black Hawk. "I will raise the white flag when they come." He silenced their protests. "You must accept this. If none join us by mid-day, I will tell our people that when the White Beaver comes we must go back."

A shout and dogs roused to full cry caught their attention. Nasomsee rode up to them.

"White men—we saw them just north of the Kyte River. Three or four hundred, all on horseback."

"The regular army? White Beaver?" asked Black Hawk.

"No, the militia."

Excitement like a gusty wind ran through the camp, for the Indians greatly feared the undisciplined militia. Quickly the chiefs moved toward Black Hawk.

"I will send three men bearing the white flag. You Bee Hunter, and you," pointing at a young warrior, "and you, Whirling Thunder."

The young men stepped forward. From a wad of white cloth someone handed him, Black Hawk tore a square. Whirling Thunder fastened it to his lance.

"Go to the Long Knives," said Black Hawk. "Bring their

chiefs here. Say that we want to go back down the Rock River. If they are in camp, then return and I will go to them. Be gone."

In a whirl of dust and thudding hoofs, the three young warriors galloped away. Then Black Hawk called five of his spies, among them Bear Cub and Nasomsee. He gave them instructions to watch from a distance how the three were treated.

While the golden light of late afternoon lay across the prairie flowers of May, Black Hawk waited. He and Neapope were preparing more white flags when three of the five young men came back. Bear Cub was the first, then Nasomsee. They leaped from their ponies and stood before Black Hawk.

"Those you sent us to watch have been taken prisoners. The white flag was not honored," said Bear Cub.

"Not honored," cried Black Hawk, a length of white cloth dangling from his hand.

"As many as twenty men galloped toward us," said Nasomsee. "We got away, though they pursued us."

"Where are the others?" asked Black Hawk as the third young man came riding into camp.

"Dead," said Nasomsee. 'Their horses were not fast enough. I saw them fall when I looked back."

Black Hawk ripped the white flag in two and threw it from him.

"If this is the way they receive the white flag, our people must be avenged."

The men ran for their horses. The women hurried to bring guns, ammunition, and war clubs. There were too few warriors, Black Hawk knew. Once the failure of their hopes had begun, many of the young men started ranging over the countryside, taking a few scalps here and there as they foraged for food.

Only forty men gathered around Black Hawk. He gave a loud war whoop and led them off across the prairie. Nasomsee riding at his father's side shouted what he knew of the enemy's surroundings. He had seen them heading toward a large grove of trees.

"They'll camp there," yelled Black Hawk. "Good cover."

He led the warriors on, making no attempt to conceal their approach.

"Let them think more of us are coming," he shouted.

A number of white men came boldly riding out at the sight of the Indians. Black Hawk lifted his arm and shouted, "Revenge—wanton murder—revenge."

The cries of "Revenge, revenge," rose in a long scream from the throats of the Sauk as their horses leaped ahead in wild-eyed response.

Black Hawk, discovering that many men were now streaming toward them, signalled again. The warriors pulled their skittish horses to a standstill, slipped to the ground, and took cover behind bushes. On rushed the militia. As Black Hawk and his men tensed for their attack, the white men faltered and drew their horses to an uncertain halt some distance from the Indians.

"Now," said Black Hawk softly. He lifted his willow whistle hanging from the cord around his neck and blew a piercing blast. With those wild howls that so curdled white men's blood, they leaped onto their horses and plunged forward, firing as they rode.

Their fire was returned. Suddenly they saw one man whirl his horse about. Then another and another turned and fled before their charging advance. A few stood their ground, but on the open prairie they were an easy mark. One by one they fell.

Whooping, half laughing in delight at this unexpected turn of affairs, they gave chase. In the panic of desperation, the militia rode toward the grove. Close behind them came the Sauk.

Now. Now they will take their stand, thought Black Hawk,

firing again. He saw the rider tumble from his horse. Nasom-see grasped the bridle and dragged the horse along with him until a warrior, leaping free from his own dying mount, grasped the bridle from him.

Even in the grove the militia took no stand, but galloped furiously on through their own camp, scattering their comrades. Men scrambled for the nearest horse, or rolled out of the way and fled into the woods on foot, hoping only to save their own scalps.

Night had come but with it the moon. Its light magnified and distorted every shadowy shape. All was wild confusion.

With no one left to fight, the battle ended. A few of the warriors continued the pursuit but the rest turned back, gathering a stray horse here and there, trimming off a scalp lock, or taking note of the plunder.

All the prairie was silvered and calm under the moon's benign light. Assessing their losses, Black Hawk found that only a few men had been killed. During the battle in the grove Black Hawk had caught a glimpse of Bee Hunter and heard Whirling Thunder's wild cry, and knew then that they would return.

Content, the warriors jogged toward the camping ground.

"Tomorrow we will go back to bury our dead," said Black Hawk.

"There will be much plunder," said Neapope.

"And food, they left everything behind."

"I am astonished at the way they ran when we were such a small party. If this is the way they fight, maybe——"

"These are not the regular army," said Black Hawk. "*They* might have honored our white flag."

"Yet this should put heart into the Potawatomi," said Neapope.

"It might be worth trying again to rally the Potawatomi," said Black Hawk, striking his thigh. "I'll go to Shabona's village and try once more."

In order that all might share, Black Hawk sent out messengers to recall the raiding parties. Then at dawn they returned to the battleground. Nasomsee lifted the fingers of one hand twice, then held up one finger.

"That many stood and fought," he said.

"A brave warrior, this leader. The rest of them ran like kicked dogs," said Black Hawk scornfully.

Neapope took a knife from his belt and slid loose a bloody scalp, then sliced the knife across the body's neck.

"That will show the white men who they fight against," he said, and others followed his example, mutilating the enemy even as they tenderly laid aside their own dead for burial.

They ransacked wagons and knapsacks, bundling all that would be useful into blankets to carry back to camp. There were saddles, rifles, ammunition, and food. The women would be pleased and the children would stand waiting with greedy looks, and watering mouths, and scrawny bodies.

"These wagons are stuck fast in the mud," said Bear Cub, pulling at a wheel.

Whirling Thunder beat upon the empty whiskey barrels.

"They must have drunk all this to save it."

"Many were already drunk when we brought in the white flag," said Bee Hunter, "but it did not make them bold."

When the plunder had been divided, Black Hawk hurried to visit Shabona, some distance to the southeast. His war talk was rejected by this great Potawatomi leader.

"There is no hope for a union of the tribes," said Shabona. We have learned that. There is nothing left for us but to be friends with them."

"It may even be too late for that when they do not honor our flag of truce."

Shabona did not answer and Black Hawk, hurrying back to his people, knew desperation. Somehow they must reach a place of safety.

12. The Flight Begins

Black Hawk reported his failure to the anxiously waiting chiefs.

"Now," he said, "this is what we must do. Canoes will continue up the Rock. Chiefs Pamaho and Atako take fifty warriors and go with them—fast. Protect them if necessary."

The two chiefs nodded.

"Our mounted forces will go up the Kishwaucokee. We will take no trouble to cover our trail."

"Ah—they will think you go to the headquarters of the Fox in Illinois country," said Pamaho quickly.

"Then we will turn north again, scattering out over many trails. Then head back and join our people at the island in Lake Koshkonong."

"We can only hope no Winnebago will betray us," said Pamaho.

"Trust the gods," said Black Hawk. "Surely some of the Winnebago will fool the Long Knives for us."

Word was spread among the people. The women began rolling up mats and bundles, gathering cooking pots, getting all ready before snatching a few hours sleep.

Within the circle of firelight, Black Hawk found his women bending over Namequa's little girl. Namequa's small boy, his face set in a struggle for manhood, stood beside them looking down at the huddled group.

"The sickly one," said Singing Bird.

"Dead," said Namequa, her eyes burning and dry in the blank mask of her face.

"Bury her," said Black Hawk, not daring even to touch Namequa's arm, and added bitterly, "There is time at least for that." Then he told them quickly they were moving on.

He turned away to go among the people, encouraging them, answering the women's questions, trying to allay the fears and accusations their eyes revealed but their lips withheld. Namequa had a right to think as they did now, yet she too had held her tongue.

Before first light, Pamaho and Atako were hurrying the people into the canoes. When Black Hawk saw that all were embarked, he gave the signal and the mounted warriors moved out. They left a waste of trampled grass dotted with the ashes of many fires, discarded bones, a few useless rags, and freshly-made graves, hastily done—the last service for children and old people who could go no farther.

The warriors moved up Kishwaucokee, the trails they left confusing as to direction. At upper Kishwaucokee, Chief Four Legs and several Winnebagos appeared. They reported that white soldiers were searching around the headwaters of the Fox and that White Beaver was moving slowly up river from Dixon's Ferry.

"You will be safe for a time on the Koshkonong," said the Winnebago, Black Wolf.

"Fishing and hunting is good there, I hear," said Black Hawk. "My people are tired and hungry."

"We know the trails," said Four Legs. "We will send guides with you."

It was June, the first flowering moon. The prairies were ablaze with grass flowers when the Winnebago guides led Black Hawk and his warriors to Koshkonong.

Here, on an island in the northern end of the lake, the people camped in some comfort. Children and women were spearing fish for the lake was full of pike, bass and catfish. The men set traps.

They lingered in temporary safety. When the wild roses burst into full bloom, Black Hawk's spies reported the militia was roaming at large, raiding and plundering Indian villages, and that the army still intended to follow them. Now the few Kickapoo, Winnebago and Potawatomi who had joined them were deserting Black Hawk.

Bold young warriors of Black Hawk's band whipped up a following and small raiding parties scattered out in search of provisions—anything to sustain their dependents. Black Hawk made no attempt to stop them. He himself led out two hundred warriors, laid siege to Apple River Fort and, at Kellog's Grove, sent white soldiers scurrying for protection. Plunder was what they needed now, not scalps.

"We have run the bear into his hole," said Black Hawk. "Let us be satisfied with that."

"The only good white man is a dead one," said Neapope rebelliously.

Others were reporting successful raids. Gleefully rubbing his hands together, smirking and licking his lips, the Prophet told how his party had attacked and killed four men. It is as if he tasted the blood, thought Black Hawk with disgust.

"LeClaire escaped," said the Prophet.

Black Hawk concealed his relief and turned away, calling over his shoulder, "Do not dance the scalps in camp. Two of our own chiefs are dead, and seven of our warriors."

Spies reported both militia and army preparing to move. Black Hawk did not dare stay longer at Koshkonong. He led his people north and camped in the marshy area at the head of the Rock River. There he could not close his ears to the whimpering of hungry children. The exhausted, sad faces of the Old Ones haunted him day and night.

Two days later Bear Cub and Bee Hunter came in, accompanied by a Winnebago. He reported that three days before the army had reached Turtle Village. They had mingled with the Winnebago unrecognized by white men as Sauk. Later they had followed the army to the Koshkonong and left them searching that area.

"What more?" asked Black Hawk.

"The one-eyed Chief Decori will send you news. He says you must decide whether you want to go to the Four Lakes or not. Soon it might be too late."

There was little game or fish. They were too far from settlements to raid and plunder. However diligently the women hunted for roots, wild potato, crooked root, and bear potato, there was not enough.

Next day Decori himself rode into camp accompanied by Black Wolf, Chaetar and two Winnebago warriors.

The men sat on their haunches talking, as Decori scratched a map in the mud.

"We must get to the Four Lakes," said Black Hawk.

Decori's good eye blinked.

"It is time. White Beaver still searches around Koshkonong, going to the White Water and the Burnt Village, and then back again to Koshkonong."

"Can we avoid them? We must go below Koshkonong before we can turn toward the Four Lakes," said Black Hawk, touching the place on the mud map.

"Wait two days. I will tell White Beaver you are farther down the Rock."

"You think he will turn back?"

"He trusts me. I will be very sure and solemn."

"Meanwhile we start slowly down river."

"Until I send a runner to you that they are turning back— then go swiftly. Chaetar will guide you. Do not let the canoes get too far ahead."

Decori rose and, refusing the food they offered, set out with Black Wolf and one of the two Winnebago warriors to go as far as possible before night set in. Chaetar stayed behind with Black Hawk.

In two days, they started. Black Hawk, leading the warriors, moved cautiously. Spies were sent out in various directions as they advanced. They drew close to Koshkonong and Atako held back the canoes. No Winnebago runner had appeared. Black Hawk brought his people to a halt. He was about to send someone ahead to spy when down the trail came a horseman, riding hard.

Reaching them, Black Wolf pulled his lathered horse to a standstill.

"We could not trust a runner. I came myself. Twice Decori has told them you are farther down the Rock. They went farther down. Now all has changed."

"How so?"

"White Beaver is building a fort at Koshkonong while he waits for more men and supplies."

"We must turn west at once," said Black Hawk. "Abandon the canoes."

"Chaetar and I will lead you," said Black Wolf.

At a sign from Black Hawk, Atako and Pamaho brought their canoes to shore. Quickly he explained.

"Scatter the canoes along the shore so they will think they belong to us," suggested Black Wolf.

"The lighter ones can be carried," said Atako.

"See to it," said Black Hawk.

Black Wolf sent the Winnebago, who had stayed with the Sauk on his previous visit, back to Decori with instructions to tell White Beaver that Black Hawk had again gone up the Rock River.

Canoes were abandoned. Horsemen plunged into the river. Soon all were across and heading west. Black Hawk and the chiefs drove the people mercilessly now. Fear set the pace. Only later would the women dare lag behind to dig for roots.

In the late afternoon Black Wolf thought it safe to let the people rest. Black Hawk agreed, then ordered that a horse be killed.

"I will see to it," said Crouching Eagle. "They cannot march on empty stomachs."

Next day the march continued. The country was rough, wooded, and in spots swampy, making travel difficult and slow. At last they made camp on the Fourth Lake, Mendota.

There was little game around the swampy Four Lakes country, and few fish, so again the people were forced to scrape bark from trees and dig for roots.

They were resting with hungry stomachs. Black Hawk noticed Singing Bird's drawn face and the way her eyes sunk deeper and deeper. Now, when she did not know he was looking she sat humped over, a weary hand supporting her forehead.

That night Namequa came to Black Hawk.

"Make her eat something, Father," she said. "She gives what she finds to children or an Old One who will die anyway."

"That is like Singing Bird."

"She only looks at me when I talk to her."

Black Hawk stared into the fire, seeing Singing Bird's face as he had known it in the days before white men had brought them such trouble.

"When I have another horse killed," he said, "You must see that she takes her share. I would speak to her, but she would only bring me a piece of whatever she had."

"She would be right, Father."

"A warrior is used to fasting, my child." They were both silent a moment, then Black Hawk said, "My grandson?"

"The young warrior does well, Father," said Namequa. "He is like you."

She pulled her ragged blanket tight across her breast and for some moments looked off around the camp. Her voice was soft and controlled when at last she spoke again.

"We must not grieve for the little one, Father."

A gesture of her hand took in all those around them. Black Hawk nodded. She turned away quickly then and left him.

In the morning a Winnebago messenger reported that the army was on the move. Black Hawk called the chiefs.

"We must get our people to the other side of the Mississippi," said Black Hawk.

"We could go down the Wisconsin River," said Neapope.

Pamaho looked at Black Wolf, saying, "If the Winnebago will let us have some of their canoes?"

"They will," said Black Wolf.

"We were able to carry but a few of ours. All may be left behind before we reach the Wisconsin," said Atako.

"The Winnebago will help us," said the Prophet.

"We've had proof of that," said Black Hawk. "Neapope, you take twenty men and guard our rear. When we near the river, go back and spy. If they are close, send word."

That morning when the march began it was a ragged, disorderly movement. If the enemy found their trail, as they must eventually, it would be difficult to keep ahead of them. Led by the chiefs they spread out in many lines, then drew together again in one large body. Their purpose was to disguise their course, and give some of the people a chance of escape.

Mist hung heavily. A penetrating rain began and continued throughout the day, adding to their misery. One after another old people dropped behind. Or a mother stopped to bury her dead baby under a hastily gathered bundle of grasses and weeds. Long treasured kettles, bowls, and mats were tossed aside.

Spies reported they were being closely followed. Black Hawk and the chiefs drove the people on. At times, Black Hawk rode back along the line, encouraging stragglers, picking up a child to relieve the mother and carrying it far ahead with him to put it down to rest until the mother caught up.

Beyond any control of the chiefs, a division of the people was beginning. Some intended to follow the Wisconsin River. Black Hawk knew that many who had once been loyal were saying openly that he had led them into disaster. He did not blame them.

By mid-afternoon they came in sight of the Wisconsin. The enemy was close behind. A runner reported Neapope and his men were fighting them off at the rear of the column.

"Atako," called Black Hawk. "You and the Prophet get the people across. Fifty warriors will stand with me on the heights."

He shouted the names of his best warriors and called for volunteers as the frantic people pushed forward like a tide in flood.

Nasomsee's brindle pony flashed across in front of his father.

"I go with you," he said fiercely.

"No, this time Whirling Thunder. You—get to the river. See to it that all our lodge gets safely across."

Nasomsee scowled but whirled his pony and was gone.

The people were spreading out along the river bank. They began rolling logs into the water, floating them across with all the children they could safely carry. Winnebago canoes appeared. Some took to them. Others, with hatchet and knives, split elm bark from large trees, eight or ten feet in length. Shaving down each end so that it was pliable, they tied it together, contriving canoes.

Horses were swimming the river with women grasping their tails. Somehow, they managed to get as far across as an island. The rest, through shallow water, was easy.

Black Hawk saw Singing Bird herding together a group of frantic, aimless women. Then he rallied his men and led them southwest to the heights, determined to hold back the enemy as long as possible.

The soldiers charged. Black Hawk blew his whistle, shouted, "Stand your ground, never yield," and the fury broke upon them.

Again and again they fired. Outnumbered and driven back, they were only gaining time, nothing more, though they spent their fiercest effort. These men were the regulars, not militia.

At last, wiping sweat from his eyes with a forearm, Black Hawk cried, "Take cover. Down into the ravine." They moved back and, at the shrill piping of his whistle, once more began firing. Again his hoarse cry went up, "Never yield, never yield."

Black Hawk felt a wetness on his leg. His horse stumbled but he jerked up its head and the animal did not fall.

Through the late afternoon, they held the Long Knives away from the river. It grew dark. The enemy no longer pressed close. The people had had time enough to cross.

Black Hawk called out, "Enough. Scatter. Join our people. If they attack us we will fight again at the river."

The order was passed along and, in the deepening night, the warriors came together by the river.

"Bear Cub," said a man identifying himself as he rode in.

"You were with Neapope. Where is he?"

"With the Winnebago by now, or before morning," replied Bear Cub scornfully. "He said he was going up on the heights as near as he could get to the white men's camp. He intends to shout at them we will not fight if they let us cross the Mississippi. I think he plans not to return."

"Again he betrays us," said the Prophet.

Black Hawk made no comment. At his order the warriors urged their horses into the river, slipped from their backs, and swam beside them.

On the other side, far back from the river, a bedraggled group waited. Some were busy gathering wood and building rafts even in darkness. A number of the men told Black Hawk they had decided to go down the Wisconsin as some of the others had done.

"The Wisconsin is too close to white people, but it is your decision if you wish to try it," he said.

Black Hawk joined his own family and told Singing Bird and Namequa what he planned. He did not ask his sons what they preferred. He knew they would go where he led them.

"We must be gone by morning," he said to the chiefs when they gathered about him. He turned to the Winnebago men upon whom they had depended.

"I think it best to push on to the Mississippi. Chaetar, Black Wolf, will you guide us?"

"We will guide you," said Black Wolf.

"Depend on us," said Chaetar.

13. Escape From Slaughter

At sunset on the third day, Black Hawk rode to the top of a low hill. There he could look back over the way they had come. He shaded his eyes, all his being sharpened to read whatever message the distance held for him.

There was no sign yet of pursuit, no smoke from any campfire—only the vultures soaring so gracefully on the updrafts, their sharp, greedy eyes searching the earth where his people had passed.

So many had died of hunger or from wounds. Some of the living had been left behind, so weak they soon would die. Follow the vultures, white man, said Black Hawk to himself with bitter grief. What other sign do you need to know our trail, unless it be the stink of rotting flesh.

The thought of how he must drive his people on sickened Black Hawk. With lowered head and covered eyes, his soul called on the Great Spirit—yet he sat erect and watchful, not lifting his hands high, nor feeling the muscles of his horse move under him as the animal stretched its neck to crop the grass.

The people must rest, but at first light find what food they could—old acorns, roots, the slippery inner coating of bark, anything their hungry stomachs would accept.

Black Hawk rode down and left his horse where the dwindling herd cropped the scanty vegetation. Quietly then, he walked among the people. They slept huddled together where they had dropped down. Every aching muscle of his own body was repeated a thousand times over in his followers.

There was no attempt now to make a shelter with the mats. Occasionally, those still strong enough to drag the bundles had unrolled them and spread the mats under and over the old and sick. Others shuddered in hot or chilly dampness, clutching their rags and misery about them.

Children sprawled in exhaustion, twitching now and then with troubled, hungry dreams. There were no dogs yapping on their trail now. All had been eaten.

The vultures had little to pick at on the bones of the horse they had killed in the morning. Enough strength was regained for the people to struggle on. Day after endless day, step by step, they advanced. Fear and the determination of their chiefs drove them on.

They travelled in three parallel columns. As one tired, bloody foot followed another, they wore the trail deeper and deeper, so that the last one travelled in a rut from two to six inches deep. Where they passed closer together through marshy ground, it was as if a road had been dried by their passing.

"How much farther to the river, Black Hawk?" asked Singing Bird one night after the others slept.

"Too far," he said. "Chaetar and Black Wolf say two more days. We must go faster tomorrow."

Singing Bird rubbed her sore feet and said, "My moccasins, Black Hawk, they are gone."

"You must ride behind me for a while tomorrow."

"No, you must be with the warriors."

"Only if we feel sure they are far behind us, then."

"Surely they will not follow us through this awful country," she said hopefully.

"They follow, but we do not know how close."

146

"I will manage then," said Singing Bird firmly. "I'll bind my feet with—something."

One desperate day followed another. At last, far ahead a cry went up and passed back down the line.

"Look, look. It is the river. The river."

They had seen the mists that lay over the Great River on that hot and hazy day of August. Renewed hope enlivened them, quickened their pace, even brought smiles. Descending a steep bluff, they came down into the thickly wooded bottom land.

They ran forward over the soggy, weed-tangled land, stumbling through the underbrush and fallen timber. Wading through stagnant, green-scummed pools they reached the banks of the Mississippi. On the other side lay safety. Tears ran down the faces of the women, and coursed along the wrinkles of the Old Ones. Every agonized breath drawn was a half-sob.

The chiefs shouted orders, yet no one had to be directed what to do, so urgent was their need. They began dragging logs and chopping at young trees so they might make rafts.

Chaetar and Nasomsee scouted up and down the river in each direction, but found no Winnebago canoes. Black Wolf was sure they had been promised. Something had gone wrong.

Black Hawk called the chiefs to hasty council.

"There is no safety here without canoes," he said. "We can't get everyone across before they catch up with us."

"Then we must fight if they come," said Crouching Eagle.

"Better to get away," said Black Hawk. "We can hide among friendly Winnebago—get across farther up."

There was a dissenting murmur, then cries of "No, no," came from nearly all the chiefs. Many women only lifted their eyes as they continued to cut long wands of grass for twisting into ropes to tie together the shaky rafts they hoped would carry them to safety.

147

"Smaller parties might have more chance," Black Hawk conceded. "Very well then, those of you who can, get across."

By mid-afternoon a few lucky ones had crossed and others were on their way. Then Namequa, searching up river for ropy weeds, cried, "Look, look. Smoke—a boat."

Everyone stared where she pointed.

"The *Warrior*," exclaimed Black Hawk, shading his eyes. "I know her captain. Do not shoot," he commanded.

"They will fire on us," cried Crouching Eagle.

"The white flag," shouted Black Hawk. "We'll try the white flag again."

Black Hawk tore a piece of dirty white cloth from a child's shoulders. Threading it onto a stick he held it high and waved toward the approaching *Warrior*.

"It's our chance. We can save our women and children."

The boat drew closer and Black Hawk shouted, "Captain Throckmorton, Captain Throckmorton. Send your canoe and I will come aboard. I am Black Hawk."

One they recognized as a Winnebago called out, "Captain says 'Are you Winnebago'?"

"Black Wolf, tell him we want to give ourselves up to the captain."

Bear Cub had jumped into the river, carrying a white flag and was swimming toward the *Warrior*.

There was running to and fro on the boat. The Winnebago cupped his mouth, shouting at them.

"Run," cried Black Wolf. "They are going to fire."

Women threw themselves to the ground or scuttled to hide behind a log or tree, dragging their children with them. Whirling Thunder leaped into the river and swam to Bear Cub, hauling him back as the first blast of shot came from the *Warrior*.

Like scattering leaves in a windstorm, the Indians took cover. From behind trees and fallen logs, they returned fire. For an hour or more this went on, Black Hawk and the chiefs shouting their defiance, encouraging the warriors. Then slowly the boat swung out into midstream and drew away.

"Strange they leave now," said Whirling Thunder.

"They may intend to let us cross," said Black Hawk hopefully.

The chiefs and people moved toward Black Hawk.

"That Winnebago could not have told him the truth," said Black Hawk. "That captain would not have fired on an honorable enemy who sought to surrender."

The Prophet wiped blood from a wound on his arm.

"You believe the lies of these white men, Black Hawk."

"There are those of our own people as well who lie," snapped Black Hawk, flashing an angry glance at him.

The Prophet continued as if he had not heard.

"The white people do not consider us honorable enemies, but only dirty scum whose word is nothing. So how do you expect to be treated when they catch us?"

Black Hawk said nothing.

"Twenty-three dead," reported Bear Cub.

A wail split the momentary silence.

"It is Crouching Eagle's woman," said Namequa who stood nearby, wiping mud from hands and arms. "He is dead."

"Crouching Eagle!" exclaimed Black Hawk, still staring after the *Warrior*, and muttering to himself, "Crouching Eagle—beside me so many years."

"I wonder if the boat will return," said Atako.

Black Hawk drew a hand over his face and came back to his place with them, looking sadly around at his people.

"Sometimes they use up their wood," he said.

"It will be too dark soon to see us," said Pamaho.

"We cannot be sure they will let us alone," said Black Hawk. "We have lost much daylight time. I still think it would be best to move north. Those of you who wish to may follow me. We will hide for a time among the Winnebago."

149

Chaetar and Black Wolf were nodding approval, but among the people there was dissent.

"More chance now if we scatter," said Bee Hunter.

"Very well then," said Black Hawk. "Cross here if you can get across. Those who will go with me, stand aside."

He moved to a small hillock. Only five lodges chose to join him. His own family and some of their relatives, the Prophet and his followers, Bear Cub, Atako and Pamaho and their people. Many of the chiefs and their lodges who might have followed him were dead.

Black Hawk led his diminished band up river. When they had gone a safe distance he called a halt. Chaetar and Black Wolf stood beside him.

"We will go north as far as we can go before darkness. Black Wolf and Chaetar know this country. Bear Cub, you and Nasomsee, go back and find out if the army still pursues us. In the morning, return and tell us what you have discovered."

Drawing Pamaho and Atako aside he said, "I am worried. I do not feel sure I am wise to leave our people."

"It is their own choice," said Atako, somewhat testily.

"Our few warriors could not turn back an army," said Pamaho.

"But together?" said Black Hawk with lifted eyebrows.

"Too late," said Pamaho. "Better to get away."

They prepared a makeshift camp in an oak opening when they could go no farther. It was a protected spot, distant enough from the river so that they dared build fires to dry their mud-soaked garments.

In the morning Bear Cub returned. The army was still approaching the river.

"Bee Hunter and I found them. I ran into him on the way. He will tell those at the river to send back a rear guard."

"Well done," said Black Hawk. "Now we must do this."

He pointed at Atako. "You and the Prophet stay here and protect our people. Whirling Thunder count off fifty men. You, Nasomsee and Bear Cub will lead us toward the enemy. We will see what we can do to put them off the trail. You who remain behind, move on up river. We will return to you."

They chose the best horses and set out. As they rode, Black Hawk made his plan and passed the word among them.

"We will make a false trail. That place near the Bad Axe where we turned left to approach the river. There we can make a new trail off to the right."

When they reached the spot no soldiers were yet in sight. They soaked their blankets in a soggy bit of marsh and dragged them across the trail until Black Hawk cried, "Enough."

Then horses and men struck off to the right from the old trail. Some distance farther along Black Hawk dispersed his men in hiding.

"When you hear my gun, fire, but only enough to draw them on as we move back."

Soon the first of the troops began to appear. They had followed the new trail without hesitation. Black Hawk grinned at Whirling Thunder, saying, "White Beaver is not so smart," and raised his gun.

The troops followed them. A man or two of the Long Knives fell. Still the Sauk drew them on. Then they heard gun fire begin far on their right.

Bear Cub crept through bushes to reach Black Hawk.

"A messenger has come to them. They are turning back."

"Must have found the main trail," said Black Hawk. "Go that way. See if it will be possible for us to get through. Do not be discovered, return to me. We must know if it is more of the enemy that fires over there—or our own people."

Bear Cub slid away. Black Hawk and his men moved slowly back in the direction from which they had come.

Bear Cub returned and said, "I went up on the bluff. Soldiers are everywhere. They must have come from many directions. We cannot get through."

"You are sure?"

"There are hundreds of them—everywhere. There must have been more than the army we knew followed us."

"Back then," said Black Hawk and, with Chaetar at his side, led the way to his own little band, anxious to move them beyond danger.

At dawn the next morning Bee Hunter stumbled into their camp, exhausted but unharmed.

"It was no fight," he told them. "It was slaughter."

The people crowded around to listen.

"All my lodge is dead. My wife and children were shot as they tried to swim the river. We would have done better to come with you, Black Hawk. There must have been a thousand soldiers. We had sent back a rear guard of seventy men——"

"Ah, that was their guns we heard," said Black Hawk. "We should have got through to them."

"Only a lone man could have got through," said Bee Hunter.

"I should have been that one," cried Black Hawk.

"What good would it have done to lose you as well as Crouching Eagle?" said Bear Cub.

"Tell us the rest," said Black Hawk sadly.

"The Sioux had come and tomahawked them as they came out on the other side of the river," said Bee Hunter. "I shot from behind a dead horse for a while. I killed eight men— at least eight. But no scalps."

His face twisted in a horrible grimace.

"Our people tried to give themselves up. They paid no attention. The women were swimming the river with the children on their backs. I saw a soldier shoot at one. I killed him."

Bee Hunter dropped wearily to the ground.

"What more?" said Black Hawk.

"I was out of ammunition, so I stayed quiet there under the river bank. The *Warrior* came back again. It fired on those in the water." He was silent for a moment, then said, "The river was red—yes, red with our blood, not with the fires of sunset, but with our blood."

His voice broke, and among the women a keening and moaning began. It threatened to rise higher and higher. Black Hawk turned on them.

"Silence," he cried, his voice harsh. "Do you want to bring them upon us?" In his grief at what he had heard he had spoken savagely, but now he said more gently, "Our sorrow is too great for this. Besides it is too dangerous here."

Black Wolf stepped forward.

"You must hide among our people. Decori will welcome you. There are so few of you now you will be safe."

"Where is safe now?" asked Black Hawk and did not expect an answer, nor did any of his people give one.

14. Surrender

Black Hawk, just out of the water, rested by the river. He was dressed only in breechclout and moccasins, and the tinkling baubles in his ears that Singing Bird thought became a war chief, though one discredited and in hiding. Chief Decori sat beside him in brooding silence. Black Hawk, half dozing now in the heat of the August afternoon and lulled by the monotonous buzzing of late summer insects, had found peace.

Black Wolf appeared a little distance away. Decori beckoned him to them and he came to sit cross legged beside them. Black Hawk looked up, startled that he had let himself relax his guard this much.

"I bring news," said Black Wolf. "The two Winnebagos who were with the white soldiers say they left before Neapope shouted from the heights—if he did so."

Black Hawk lifted a hand and let it drop.

"So we may never know the truth—and never from Neapope."

"There is more. A reward is offered for you, Black Hawk. These same men told me a Potawatomi said you were thought to be somewhere among the Winnebago."

Decori's gnarled old forefinger came up to point at Black Wolf.

"I did not tell them he was with us."

"What reward do they offer?" asked Decori.

"One hundred dollars money, and twenty ponies."

"I would not betray you, Black Hawk," said Decori. "Nor any of my village."

Black Hawk bowed his head in acknowledgment.

"Our women would tear the betrayer to pieces," said Black Wolf. "Do you know that they are working on a handsome deerskin dress for you?"

Black Hawk smiled. Singing Bird had told him too of how the women, not presuming to approach him, had lavished their regard for him in kindness to all the women of their ragged band.

"I cannot remain hidden much longer," said Black Hawk. "Some day the shadow of a stranger will appear beyond the trees——"

He lifted his hand in the gesture of resignation. The two old friends regarded each other speculatively. Then Black Hawk spoke.

"Why should you not be the one?"

Decori looked shocked and hurt, until Black Hawk smiled at him, saying, "This cannot last. It is time to surrender. Then why should you not be the one to profit?"

Decori stared thoughtfully across the river.

"It is not good for your people, my being sheltered here. Wouldn't you like twenty ponies, Decori, and much money?"

Decori chuckled, his one good eye twinkling.

"Think how favorably the Long Knives would look upon such loyalty to them," said Black Hawk.

"Ah yes, my people need their favor."

"It is small enough payment for all the risks you have taken for us. Better if it were fifty horses.

"Fifty horses would be much more respectful to you," said Decori.

Black Hawk agreed, then said, "Do this on one condition only—share with Chaetar and Black Wolf.

"Agreed then," said Decori. "But you must rest and feast for one more day before we start."

The old chief pulled himself stiffly erect, saying, "Tomorrow we will make our plans," and left with Black Wolf.

The next day, as Decori again rested on the river bank, Black Hawk came to him. When Decori saw that Black Hawk carried the ancient otter skin bag with its porcupine quill decorations, he rose and stood erect. Black Hawk spoke.

"I have brought you my sacred war bundle left to me by my father. Keep it for me. It is the soul of the Sauk nation. It has never been dishonored in battle. Take it. It is my life—dearer to me than life."

"I will guard it for you, Black Hawk. And when the time comes I will return it to you."

"I will give myself up to the Americans, and if—so be it."

"If the Great Spirit permits you to live, I will return this sacred bundle to you."

"It has not left my care since my father died in battle. If I too am to die—Whirling Thunder must receive it."

"I am honored by your trust."

These ceremonial matters attended to, the two old friends sat side by side.

"We could send the women and children across the Mississippi," said Decori. "They could find the way back to your people and be safe."

"I have considered that," said Black Hawk. "Some are willing, but Singing Bird says she will not go."

"Do you have no command over her?"

"Singing Bird is a very strong-minded woman," said Black Hawk.

"Perhaps if you had taken another wife——"

"He who has had Singing Bird does not want another woman," said Black Hawk. "Anyway, she says she is going with me—if she has to follow in a canoe she steals from the

Winnebago. She says that would be a wicked thing to do when they have been so kind to all of us."

Decori acknowledged the compliment with a smile and a twitch of his good eye.

"We will start tomorrow. It is not wise to delay longer. It will take many days to reach Prairie du Chien."

Early the next morning some of Black Hawk's band started for the Mississippi. They were led by Bear Cub and Bee Hunter and accompanied by their Winnebago friends. Decori, Chaetar and Black Wolf set out with their prisoners for Prairie du Chien. Singing Bird followed her husband with Namequa and other women who would not leave their husbands.

The strongest paddlers of Decori's party set a swift pace. At times, they hid themselves in the woods and waited until the dusk of evening would give protection. When moonlight turned the river to silver, they paddled steadily on.

Some distance from Prairie du Chien, they hid their canoes along the river bank. Singing Bird, carrying the white deerskin garments the Winnebago women had made, accompanied Black Hawk when he withdrew from the others. As Singing Bird unrolled the bundle, she said, "What will happen to you, husband?"

Black Hawk slipped into the shirt-like garment that came to his knees and waited while Singing Bird tied the belt and straightened the long fringe.

"I don't know how they treat their prisoners, Singing Bird. It may be that I shall be tortured."

She gave a little cry and grasped his arms, her fingers pressing hard against the bone.

"Oh no, husband, you are a chief and an honorable man. Surely not when you have surrendered to them?"

"Do not fear for me. I will bear myself bravely. Black Hawk is not a coward."

Regardless of those who stood at a distance and turned

their faces away, Singing Bird clutched him to her and laid her head on his breast.

"I have known that for many years. But now I do not care whether you are a coward or not. I do not want anything cruel done to you. If they do—one thing—I myself will take revenge."

Black Hawk smiled and lifted her face.

"How could you do that, my little bird?"

"I will find a way. I will creep upon them. I have skinned the deer and buffalo. I could do as well by a white man. I could——"

"Hush, hush, you will do nothing of the sort. I will surrender. Then our people will be at peace."

"The white man always gets his way—always, always—" she cried passionately. "It is going to be that way as long as we live, as long as our children live, even their children."

She knelt and began tying his leggings firmly in place at the knees. He looked down at her and sadly caressed her black hair, smooth and glossy again since their stay with the Winnebago.

Singing Bird said no more. Silently, they rejoined the others.

When the sun was high, the group placed themselves in a conspicuous position on a point of land extending out into the river, Black Wolf carrying a large white flag. Moving lazily with the fitful wind it folded into shadow, or again snapped freely above them, whitened by the glaring light.

In silence, they waited. After some time, soldiers appeared from the woods on an island and stopped in surprise at the sight of them. Hurrying into their boats, the group approached the Indians. Decori stepped forward and called out.

"I am Chief Decori of the Winnebago. I have captured Black Hawk and his chiefs. We wish to go to General Street, our agent at Prairie du Chien."

They were marched to the agent's house and, after some

talk with General Street, he led the party across the prairie to the Fort. There he left the chiefs in an adjoining room and went into Colonel Taylor's office.

Decori spoke softly, saying, "I will make a speech. I am old. I may not have many more chances."

"Make a good one," murmured Black Hawk.

Decori and Black Hawk slipped across the room and stood near the doorway, hoping to catch some meaning from the strange talk within.

"Decori has brought in Black Hawk, Colonel Taylor," said Street.

"So they told me."

"They brought his sons too, and the Prophet and Atako and Pamaho. Several others—many of their women and children too."

"Good, that's the lot of them with the Sioux bringing in Neapope yesterday. We've got the ringleaders now."

"We could let all but the chiefs go, couldn't we?"

"Later. You'd better send for Keokuk to come and get them."

"Right. The old one, the one-eyed Decori, and Chaetar and Black Wolf claim they searched and searched and finally captured them with some difficulty."

Taylor snorted.

"Ah well, they want the reward, and the credit of being friendly. Let them have it."

"They hinted that Black Hawk was worth more than a measly twenty horses.

Colonel Taylor was silent for some minutes, then he said, "A pity isn't it. None of this needed to happen."

Then the Indians heard a fist bank on the table and looked at each other with startled eyes, for Decori understood little more English than Black Hawk.

"If Atkinson had had the wit and the guts to stop them before they started up river——. That affair at Sycamore

Creek touched it off. Ah well, bring the old boy in. He's caused us trouble enough. Bring 'em all in. We'll have a council."

General Street beckoned them in. Colonel Taylor rose and shook hands with them, then, seating himself, motioned to old Decori.

And so, pausing at times for the interpreter to translate, Decori spoke.

"My father, we followed the trail of these men for many miles, deep into the wilderness, through swamp and forest. When we came upon their camp, they were too exhausted to flee. Black Hawk held out his hands to be bound——"

Black Hawk, seeing Colonel Taylor lift his eyebrows and send him a quizzical glance, quickly lowered his own eyes.

"Now I bring them to you. They are our prisoners . . . My Father, you told us to get these men and it would be the cause of much good for the Winnebago . . . If you had told us to bring their heads alone, we would have done so . . . We want you to keep them safe. If they are hurt, we do not want to see it. Wait until we are gone before it is done."

Black Hawk wondered if Decori wasn't overdoing things a little, then sighed. If there was anything for Decori to gain, now was the time.

"My Father," continued Decori. "Many little birds have been flying around our ears and we thought they whispered that there was evil intended for us, but now we hope these evil birds will let our ears alone. My Father, you say you love your red children. We think we love you as much . . . We have confidence in you. My Father, we have come in haste and we are tired and hungry. We now put these men in your hands."

Colonel Taylor turned to Black Hawk.

"Does Black Hawk have anything to say?"

Black Hawk rose.

"My Father, the last sun has shone on Black Hawk. He is

161

now a prisoner, but he can stand torture. He is not afraid of death. He is no coward. He is an Indian. He has done nothing of which an Indian need be ashamed. He has fought the battles of his country against the white men who come year after year to cheat his people and take away their lands——"

Black Hawk was silent for a moment, then said, "My Father, the white men do not scalp the head, but they do worse, they poison the heart."

He paused again, remembering that he was a prisoner, so added humbly, "Black Hawk is satisfied."

General Street murmured a word or two to Taylor when the interpreter had finished and rose to address them.

"My children, you have done well . . . Chief Decori, I am sure Colonel Taylor will see that you get the reward. The money and the horses will be brought to you. The little birds will be taken care of. Colonel Taylor is a just man. More than that I am not authorized to say.

"My children, I will go down to Rock Island with the prisoners . . . Colonel Taylor will take good care of you until we start for Rock Island."

Colonel Taylor made a notation on the papers in front of him as the interpreter translated, adding August 27, 1832, and rose to speak.

"My children, our great Chief, General Scott, told me where to take the prisoners. . . . I will deliver them to him and he will do with them and use them in such manner as may be ordered by your Father, the President."

Colonel Taylor dismissed the council, and the Indians were marched away to the guard house.

A few days later, when the *Warrior* began moving downstream, Black Hawk stood on the deck. He stared toward his people who had come to see them start for prison before they themselves were delivered into the hands of Keokuk.

Black Hawk did not see Singing Bird. Then, knowing her, his eyes searched along the river bank. She stood at the water's edge in the sunlight, her figure plain to be seen against the dark foilage behind her.

He leaned forward, trying to see her face more clearly, but he could not. She half lifted her hand, and called, "Black Hawk."

Whether the words carrying over the glassy water actually reached his ears or not, Black Hawk knew that she called him. He answered under his breath, "Singing Bird, Singing Bird," then drew his lips together and gave the clear, piercing call of the hermit thrush.

Faintly from the distance came her answer.

15. Death Song

Several years later, Black Hawk sat on the bank of the Des Moines River with his back against a huge tree. Anyone passing on the trail might have thought he dozed in the golden autumnal haze.

Now and then he opened his eyes a slit and felt himself drifting with the river as it rippled steadily on to join the Mississippi, the Great River he would never travel again.

He drifted too on the river of an old man's memories, back to that day he had left Singing Bird and his people going to his winter of imprisonment in Jefferson Barracks, south of St. Louis. The indignity of the ball and chain would never leave him.

Again he saw Keokuk, magnificent in his finery, arriving the next summer for the council to be held in Fort Armstrong. There he was delivered into the hands of this chief of the Sauk—chief by the grace of General Scott and the Great White Father's government.

There had been at least twenty canoes. Two in the lead were lashed together. In them rode Keokuk and three of his wives, travelling comfortably in the shade of a canopy. Pennants and feathered decorations hung from the supporting staffs and above all floated the American's flag. The beating of drums, the wild singing was for Keokuk—not for him.

Again Black Hawk heard Keokuk speaking before the

council. Freeing his arm from the blanket so that he might gesture, he spoke the words echoing over and over in Black Hawk's memory.

". . . I have listened to the talk of our Great Father. It is true we pledged our honor for the liberty of our friends . . . Our councils were long. When we talked of their wives and children our hearts were full. Their wives and children came to see us, which made us feel like women, but we were men. The words which we sent to the Great Father were good . . . The Great Spirit made his heart big in council. We receive our brothers in friendship. I will shake hands with them and then I am done."

After the hand shaking, Major Garland had directed him sternly to conform to Keokuk's advice and be governed by his council in all things. It had been the final indignity—more than he could bear.

Remembering how he had leaped to his feet and answered in anger, Black Hawk felt a stirring of his old strength and bitterness. His lips moved, saying again, "My Father, I am a man, an old man. I will not conform to the counsels of anyone. I will act for myself. No one shall govern me. I am old, my hair is gray. I once gave counsel to my young men. Am I to conform to others? . . . I gave my word to our Great Father in Washington that I would not go to war again. I will live in peace. Why then must I listen to the counsel of Keokuk? I will always listen to my Father in Washington."

LeClaire and Keokuk had come to him, reminding him that he was a prisoner, that he could be endangering his freedom. Keokuk, with his wily talk, had smoothed things over, excused him because he was old, said he did not mean it, that he wished it to be forgotten.

Intently studying Major Garland's face, he had thought he caught some gleam of sympathy in the white man's eyes, and, reaching out for understanding, words had forced themselves from his lips—"Saukenuk—Saukenuk" and in the white man's tongue, "My home—no more."

Major Garland had stared back at him. All those in the room were suspended in momentary silence. Major Garland's eyes had clouded, his face drawing into a troubled frown. The tension between them snapped, and the Major looked away. Had there for an instant stood before him a proud human being, a man, someone more than what white men considered only a savage Indian?

Keokuk had stripped him of his dignity, as the child Keokuk had stripped him of his breechclout when they were both young. He had accepted the white man's world, submitted his body to their will and to Keokuk's—that was all. He was a Sauk. He had determined then not to think of what lay ahead. He would only remember the good days of his youth —Saukenuk, his boyhood, the years with Singing Bird and the children.

These he would remember now, sitting under the great tree, an old man. Soon the Great Spirit would come for him. Until then, he would stay here in the good house that his white neighbors had helped his sons build for him. He had chairs and a table, even mattresses for sleeping. Singing Bird had planted squash vines to twine themselves into the fence around their yard and make it as their home had always been.

Keokuk had sold still more of their lands. He had managed to have the Americans pay all the annuities directly to him. Much of the people's money was spent on Keokuk's many wives, his fine horses, his liquor, and gambling. He went everywhere well guarded, for many, at last, understood that he cared for nothing more than his own glory and power.

Black Hawk's old lips curled in scorn. Keokuk—chief of the Sauk, he who had no hereditary right to it. Ah well, he too had Major Street's favor. He had been given a cow. Black

Hawk smiled. He had done with hating now. It was too great an effort.

Neapope still hated. Embittered, he wandered from one Sauk or Fox village to another, plotting and hoping. Perhaps Neapope dreamed of succeeding where he had failed.

Black Hawk had not seen the Prophet since their last imprisonment. When they reached Prairie du Chien, the Prophet had been released to the Winnebago. And what good had come to the Winnebago through Decori—only horses and money. They too had lost their lands.

That fearful day at Bad Axe. Not yet could he understand why such an honorable man as White Beaver had given the Sioux permission to pursue his people beyond the Mississippi, killing two hundred or more, mostly women and children. Those who had gone down the Wisconsin had fared no better. There was no hiding place for those who opposed the Long Knives. His failure had destroyed his people.

I was the leader, but I do not kill women and children, thought Black Hawk. Could I have stopped the warriors who had joined me, or our own young men, from raiding if I had tried? We were starving. We searched for food. They would not have given it to us but only have sent word to the white soldiers where we were.

Black Hawk heard Namequa singing. He leaned sideways and saw that she swept and brushed the yard to keep it neat.

Namequa—more beautiful with every day. She had not taken another husband. If she married a white man would it be like the tree under which he sat—so intertwined were the ash and elm that it did not matter that neither stood straight and alone. Together they made one strong tree.

He looked upward, and the sun burnished the yellow leaves of the ash into chips of gold. Already the elm leaves were drifting earthward. Would it be with Namequa as it had been with him and Singing Bird? Two different tribes, but it had not mattered.

168

Singing Bird was bringing him a bowl of thick soup. The steaming fragrance sickened him.

"Is this the rabbit that Whirling Thunder brought this morning?" he asked.

Singing Bird nodded.

"Eat some, husband. It is very tender."

"It is good of you to bring it, but I cannot eat."

She sat down beside him and pulled the blanket closer around his rheumatic shoulder.

That morning Whirling Thunder had appeared as the sun was coming up. Singing Bird was fingering the remains of the squash vines. Black Hawk, wearing only a breechclout, was stretching his old bones in the warm sun. He had not yet dressed in the white man's garments he now wore.

Whirling Thunder strode toward them, a handsome, well-built man—a warrior and a hunter who had no pride now in anything he did.

"It is I, Whirling Thunder, the great hunter," he said, "I am again a little boy who brings in a rabbit."

Scornfully he threw it down before his mother. Remembering now how sadly Singing Bird had watched his going, Black Hawk knew he need not explain his rejection of the meal she brought him.

They sat for a time in silence until the Jersey cow that followed her like a dog, ready to nibble any tidbits she offered, came and licked the hand Singing Bird held out.

"Nasomsee?" asked Black Hawk, peering at a figure coming up the trail.

"Yes," said Singing Bird, and together, their hands lying side by side, they watched their son come staggering home from the trader's.

"My son," said Black Hawk. "The great warrior of such promise."

"He cannot forgive the white man for what they did to you. That is his trouble."

Black Hawk felt Singing Bird's hand move a little until it rested close against his.

"The Great Spirit has forgotten his red children," she said. "It is easier for Namequa—there is always work for women."

Singing Bird was right. What was there for his sons in a white man's world? Or for Namequa's son when he was grown? Sodden, whiskey-soaked forgetfulness, little else.

He sighed and stared far down the river, letting the swiftness of its flowing take him on with it. The Great Spirit knew he had done his best. By that measure he had never been defeated. Every man must make his own path and he had done what he had to do.

His days were numbered. Already he could feel his death song there in his throat, ready for the singing. Any day the Great Spirit would come for him. Let it be soon. Let it be now.

****

Black Hawk died October 3, 1838 at the age of 71.

Index

172

173